Time to face all the facts with CGP!

Make sure you know all the key concepts for
Foundation GCSE Maths with this CGP Knowledge Organiser!

We've boiled every topic down to the essentials, with step-by-step
methods and worked examples to help it all sink in.

There's also a matching Knowledge Retriever book that'll test
you on every page — perfect for making sure you know it all!

CGP — still the best! ☺

Our sole aim here at CGP is to produce the highest quality books —
carefully written, immaculately presented and dangerously close to being funny.

Then we work our socks off to get them out to you
— at the cheapest possible prices.

Contents

Section 6 —
Angles and Geometry

Section 7 —
Probability and Statistics

Published by CGP.
From original material by Richard Parsons.

Editors: Sarah George, Samuel Mann, Sean McParland, Ali Palin, Caley Simpson.

With thanks to Lauren McNaughten and Glenn Rogers for the proofreading.
With thanks to Emily Smith for the copyright research.

Printed by Elanders Ltd, Newcastle upon Tyne.
Clipart from Corel®

Text, design, layout and original illustrations © Richard Parsons 2021
All rights reserved.

Numbers and Calculations

Four Types of Numbers

	Definition	Examples
INTEGER	Whole number — can be positive, negative or zero	$-23, -7, 0, 10, 111$
SQUARE	Made by multiplying a whole number by itself	$1^2 = 1 \times 1 = 1,$ $2^2 = 2 \times 2 = 4$
CUBE	Made by multiplying a whole number by itself twice	$1^3 = 1 \times 1 \times 1 = 1,$ $2^3 = 2 \times 2 \times 2 = 8$
NEGATIVE	Numbers less than zero	$-2.5, -37, -365$

Adding and Subtracting with Negative Numbers

← lower numbers   higher numbers ⟹

-5 -4 -3 -2 -1 0 1 2 3 4 5

← this way to subtract   this way to add ⟹

Move 4 places right. $-3 + 4 = 1$

-5 -4 -3 -2 -1 0 1 2 3 4 5

When signs are next to each other:

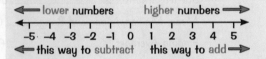

1. + + makes + $-2 + +5 = -2 + 5 = 3$

2. + − makes − $5 + -3 = 5 - 3 = 2$

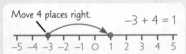

3. − + makes − $-4 - +1 = -4 - 1 = -5$

4. − − makes + $-7 - -3 = -7 + 3 = -4$

Multiplying and Dividing Negative Numbers

1. Signs the SAME — answer POSITIVE ⟹ $-3 \times -5 = +15$ $-6 \div -2 = +3$

2. Signs DIFFERENT — answer NEGATIVE ⟹ $-2 \times +7 = -14$ $+12 \div -6 = -2$

BODMAS

BODMAS gives the order of operations:

1. Brackets

'Other' is things like squaring.

2. Other

3. Division and Multiplication

4. Addition and Subtraction

EXAMPLE

Find the value of $9 - (3 + 1)^2 \times 2 + 5$.

$9 - (3 + 1)^2 \times 2 + 5$

1. $= 9 - 4^2 \times 2 + 5$

2. $= 9 - 16 \times 2 + 5$

3. $= 9 - 32 + 5$ — Work left to right when

4. $= -23 + 5$ — there's only addition and subtraction.

$= -18$

Multiplying and Dividing

Multiplying by 10, 100, etc.

1. Count the number of zeros and move the decimal point that many places BIGGER (⤴).

× by	10	100	1000
d.p. moves	1	2	3

e.g. 1.52   15.2   152.   152.

2. Add zeros before d.p. if needed.

$1.52 × 10 = 15.2$
$1.52 × 100 = 152$
$1.52 × 1000 = 1520$

Fill empty place with zero.

Dividing by 10, 100, etc.

1. Count the number of zeros and move the decimal point that many places SMALLER (⤵).

÷ by	10	100	1000
d.p. moves	1	2	3

e.g. 120   12.0   1.20   .120

2. Add or remove zeros if needed.

$120 ÷ 10 = 12$ — Remove zeros at the end.
$120 ÷ 100 = 1.2$
$120 ÷ 1000 = 0.12$ — Add zero at the start.

Multiplying and Dividing by Multiples of 10, 100, etc.

1. Multiply/divide by 1st digit of the number.

2. Count the number of zeros and move the decimal point that many places BIGGER or SMALLER.

Add/remove zeros if needed.

EXAMPLE

Calculate 24 × 400.
1. $24 × 4 = 96$
2. $96 × 100 = 9600$

Multiplying Whole Numbers

1. Line up numbers in columns.

2. Split into two multiplications.

3. Add up results from right to left.

```
①      5 6
     ×  1 2
②    1 1₁2  — 2 × 56
     5 6 0  — 10 × 56
     _____
③    6 7 2
```

Three Steps to Multiply Decimals

1. Do the multiplication with whole numbers, ignoring decimal points.

2. Count the total number of digits after the decimal points in the original numbers.

3. Make the answer have the same number of decimal places.

EXAMPLE

Work out 5.6 × 1.2.
1. $56 × 12 = 672$
2. 5.6 and 1.2 have 2 digits after the decimal points in total.
3. $5.6 × 1.2 = 6.72$

Dividing

Dividing Whole Numbers

① Put the number you're dividing inside and the number you're dividing by outside.

② Divide each digit below the line:
- Write the result above the line.
- Carry the remainder to the next digit if needed.

③ Continue until the top line is complete — this is the final answer.

What is $420 \div 15$?

① $15 \overline{)4\,2\,0}$

② $15 \overline{)4\,2\,0}$ gives 0 above — 15 won't go into 4

③ $15 \overline{)4\,2^{12}0}$ gives $0\,2$ — $42 \div 15 = 2$ remainder 12

③ $15 \overline{)4\,2^{12}0}$ gives $0\,2\,8$ — $120 \div 15 = 8$

So $420 \div 15 = 28$

Dividing a Decimal by a Whole Number

Follow the same steps as above. Put a decimal point in the answer line (right above the one below the line).

Work out $62.8 \div 4$.

$4 \overline{)6\,2\,.\,8}$ with decimal point

$4 \overline{)6^2 2\,.\,8}$ gives 1 — $6 \div 4 = 1$ remainder 2

$4 \overline{)6^2 2\,.^2 8}$ gives $1\,5\,.$ — $22 \div 4 = 5$ remainder 2

$4 \overline{)6^2 2\,.^2 8}$ gives $1\,5\,.\,7$ — $28 \div 4 = 7$

So $62.8 \div 4 = 15.7$

Three Steps to Divide by a Decimal

To divide a whole number or a decimal by a decimal:

① Write the division as a fraction.

② Multiply top and bottom by the same power of 10 to make whole numbers.

③ Do the whole number division using the method above.

Work out $49.2 \div 0.24$.

① $\dfrac{49.2}{0.24}$

You want to move the decimal point 2 places bigger.

② $= \dfrac{49.2 \times 100}{0.24 \times 100} = \dfrac{4920}{24}$

③ $24 \overline{)4\,9^1 2^{12}0}$ gives $0\,2\,0\,5$

So $49.2 \div 0.24 = 205$

Prime Numbers, Multiples and Factors

Finding Prime Numbers

PRIME NUMBER — can only be divided by itself and 1.

- First four primes are 2, 3, 5 and 7.
- To check for prime numbers between 8 and 100:

1 is NOT prime.

1) Ends in 1, 3, 7 or 9?

NO → not prime   YES → 2) Divides by 3 or 7?

This step works for checking primes between 8 and 120.

NO → PRIME   YES → not prime

1	2	3	4	5	6	7	8	9
11	12	13	14	15	16	17	18	19
21	22	23	24	25	26	27	28	29
31	32	33	34	35	36	37	38	39
41	42	43	44	45	46	47	48	49
51	52	53	54	55	56	57	58	59
61	62	63	64	65	66	67	68	69

Finding Multiples and Factors

MULTIPLE — value in a number's times table (and beyond).

FACTOR — divides into another number.

Four steps to find factors:

1) List factors in pairs, starting with $1 \times$ the number, then $2 \times$, etc.

2) Cross out pairs that don't divide exactly.

3) Stop when a number is repeated.

4) Write factors out clearly.

EXAMPLE

Find the first eight multiples of 8.

8, 16, 24, 32, 40, 48, 56, 64

EXAMPLE

Find all the factors of 20.

1) 1×20
   2×10
2) ~~$3 \times$~~
   4×5
3) 5×4
4) So the factors of 20 are:
   1, 2, 4, 5, 10, 20

Finding Prime Factors

PRIME FACTORISATION — writing a number as its prime factors multiplied together.

Three steps to use a Factor Tree:

1) Put the number at the top and split into factors.

280
28 — 10
7 4   5 2
2 2

2) Circle each prime.

3) When only primes are left, write them in order.

$280 = 2 \times 2 \times 2 \times 5 \times 7$
$= 2^3 \times 5 \times 7$

Write repeated factors as powers.

6

LCM and HCF

Lowest Common Multiple (LCM)

LCM — the smallest number that divides by all numbers in question.

Find it in two steps:

1. List multiples of each number.

2. Find the smallest that is in every list.

EXAMPLE

Find the LCM of 6 and 14.

1. Multiples of 6 are:
6, 12, 18, 24, 30, 36, (42,) 48...
Multiples of 14 are:
14, 28, (42,) 56...

2. Smallest in both is 42, so LCM = 42

LCM — Alternative Method

Find it from prime factors in two steps:

1. List all prime factors that are in either number.

(If a factor appears more than once in a number, list it that many times.)

2. Multiply together.

EXAMPLE

$8 = 2^3$ and $20 = 2^2 \times 5$.
Find the LCM of 8 and 20.

1. $8 = 2 \times 2 \times 2$ $20 = 2 \times 2 \times 5$
So prime factors in either number are 2, 2, 2, 5

2. LCM = $2 \times 2 \times 2 \times 5 = 40$

Highest Common Factor (HCF)

HCF — the biggest number that divides into all numbers in question.

Find it in two steps:

1. List factors of each number.

2. Find the biggest that is in every list.

EXAMPLE

Find the HCF of 16 and 40.

1. Factors of 16 are:
1, 2, 4, (8,) 16
Factors of 40 are:
1, 2, 4, 5, (8,) 10, 20, 40

2. Biggest in both is 8, so HCF = 8

HCF — Alternative Method

Find it from prime factors in two steps:

1. List all prime factors that are in both numbers.

2. Multiply together.

EXAMPLE

$36 = 2^2 \times 3^2$ and $60 = 2^2 \times 3 \times 5$.
Find the HCF of 36 and 60.

1. $36 = 2 \times 2 \times 3 \times 3$
$60 = 2 \times 2 \times 3 \times 5$
So prime factors in both numbers are 2, 2, 3

2. HCF = $2 \times 2 \times 3 = 12$

Fractions

Simplifying Fractions

To simplify, divide top and bottom by the same number. Repeat until they won't divide any more.

$$\frac{30}{45} = \frac{6}{9} = \frac{2}{3}$$

with $\div 5$ and $\div 3$ on top, $\div 5$ and $\div 3$ on bottom

Top and bottom numbers of a simplified fraction have no common factors.

Mixed Numbers and Improper Fractions

MIXED NUMBER — has integer part and fraction part, e.g. $2\frac{1}{3}$.

IMPROPER FRACTION — top number is larger than bottom number, e.g. $\frac{7}{5}$.

To write mixed numbers as improper fractions:

1 Write as an addition. 2 Turn integer part into a fraction. 3 Add together.

$$2\frac{3}{4} = 2 + \frac{3}{4} = \frac{8}{4} + \frac{3}{4} = \frac{11}{4}$$
①　　②　　③

To write improper fractions as mixed numbers:

1 Divide top by bottom. 2 Answer is whole number part, remainder goes on top of fraction part.

① $17 \div 3 = 5$ remainder 2
② So $\frac{17}{3} = 5\frac{2}{3}$

Multiplying and Dividing

1 Rewrite any mixed numbers as fractions.

If dividing

If multiplying

Turn 2nd fraction upside down. Change $\div$ to $\times$.

2 Multiply tops and bottoms separately.

3 Simplify using common factors.

$$1\frac{3}{5} \times \frac{3}{10} = \frac{8}{5} \times \frac{3}{10} \quad ①$$
$$= \frac{8 \times 3}{5 \times 10} \quad ②$$
$$= \frac{24}{50} = \frac{12}{25} \quad ③$$

$$\frac{7}{6} \div \frac{8}{3} = \frac{7}{6} \times \frac{3}{8} \quad ①$$
$$= \frac{7 \times 3}{6 \times 8} \quad ②$$
$$= \frac{21}{48} = \frac{7}{16} \quad ③$$

You can cancel down before doing the multiplications to make things easier.

Ordering Fractions

COMMON DENOMINATOR — a number that all denominators divide into.

1 Rewrite the fractions with a common denominator.

2 Compare the top numbers.

EXAMPLE

Put $\frac{11}{6}$, $\frac{17}{12}$ and $\frac{7}{4}$ in descending order.

LCM of 6, 12 and 4 is 12.

① $\frac{11}{6} = \frac{22}{12}$ ($\times 2$), $\frac{7}{4} = \frac{21}{12}$ ($\times 3$)

② $\frac{22}{12} > \frac{21}{12} > \frac{17}{12}$

So $\frac{11}{6}$, $\frac{7}{4}$, $\frac{17}{12}$

Fractions, Decimals and Percentages

Adding and Subtracting Fractions

① Make denominators the same.

② Add/subtract the top numbers only.

EXAMPLE

Find $1\frac{1}{3} - \frac{5}{8}$.

① $1\frac{1}{3} - \frac{5}{8} = \frac{4}{3} - \frac{5}{8} = \frac{32}{24} - \frac{15}{24}$

Rewrite any mixed numbers.

② $= \frac{32-15}{24} = \frac{17}{24}$

Finding Fractions of Amounts

① Divide it by the bottom.

② Multiply by the top.

Multiply then divide if it's easier.

$\frac{7}{12}$ of $240 = (240 \div 12) \times 7$

② $= 20 \times 7 = 140$

Expressing as a Fraction

① Write 1st number over 2nd.

② Cancel down.

210 as a fraction of 75

① $\frac{210}{75}$ $\overset{\div 3}{=}$ $\frac{70}{25}$ $\overset{\div 5}{=}$ $\frac{14}{5}$

② $\div 3$ $\div 5$

Common Conversions

Fraction	Decimal	Percentage
$\frac{1}{2}$	0.5	50%
$\frac{1}{4}$	0.25	25%
$\frac{3}{4}$	0.75	75%
$\frac{1}{3}$	0.3333...	$33\frac{1}{3}\%$
$\frac{2}{3}$	0.6666...	$66\frac{2}{3}\%$

Fraction	Decimal	Percentage
$\frac{1}{10}$	0.1	10%
$\frac{1}{5}$	0.2	20%
$\frac{1}{8}$	0.125	12.5%
$\frac{3}{8}$	0.375	37.5%
$\frac{5}{2}$	2.5	250%

How to Convert

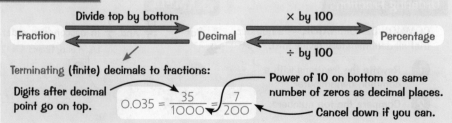

Fraction —— Divide top by bottom —→ Decimal —— × by 100 —→ Percentage

Decimal ←— ÷ by 100 —— Percentage

Terminating (finite) decimals to fractions:

Digits after decimal point go on top.

$0.035 = \frac{35}{1000} = \frac{7}{200}$

Power of 10 on bottom so same number of zeros as decimal places.

Cancel down if you can.

Rounding Numbers

Two Steps to Round to Decimal Places

1. Identify the position of the **last digit** in the rounded number.
2. Look at the digit to the right — the **decider**.

- If the decider is **5 or more**, **round up** the last digit.
- If the decider is **4 or less**, **leave the last digit** as it is.

To round up a 9, replace it with 0 and add 1 to the digit on the left.

EXAMPLE

Round 8.6351 to 2 decimal places.

1. 8.6(3)51 — Circle the last digit.
2. The decider is 5, so the last digit rounds up to 4.

8.6351 = 8.64 (2 d.p.)

Three Steps to Round to Significant Figures

The **1st significant figure (s.f.)** is the first digit that **isn't zero**. Each digit after it (including zeros) is another significant figure.

1. Identify the position of the **last digit** in the rounded number.
2. Look at the digit to the right — the **decider**.

- If the decider is **5 or more**, **round up** the last digit.
- If the decider is **4 or less**, **leave the last digit** as it is.

3. Fill spaces **before** the decimal point with **zeros**.

EXAMPLE

Round 732.5 to 1 significant figure.

1. (7)32.5 — Circle the last digit.
2. The decider is 3, so the last digit stays as it is.
3. 732.5 = 700 (1 s.f.)

Fill 2 spaces with zeros.

Three Steps to Round to the Nearest...

... whole number, ten, hundred, etc.

1. Identify the position of the last digit in the rounded number. *Units place, tens place, etc.*
2. Look at the digit to the right — the decider.

- If the decider is **5 or more**, **round up** the last digit.
- If the decider is **4 or less**, **leave the last digit** as it is.

3. Fill spaces **before** the decimal point with **zeros**.

EXAMPLE

Round 347 to the nearest ten.

1. 3(4)7 — Circle the last digit.
2. The decider is 7, so the last digit rounds up to 5.
3. 347 = 350 (to nearest 10)

Fill space with zero.

Estimating and Rounding Errors

Estimating Calculations

1 Round numbers to 1 or 2 significant figures.

2 Work out answer using rounded numbers.

3 If you're asked, say whether your value is an underestimate or overestimate.

EXAMPLE

Estimate the value of $\dfrac{18 + 7.6}{4.2}$.

Is this an underestimate or overestimate?

$$\frac{18 + 7.6}{4.2} \approx \frac{20 + 8}{4} = \frac{28}{4} = 7$$

≈ means 'approximately equal to'.

3 The top numbers round up and the bottom number rounds down. The number being divided is bigger and the number it's being divided by is smaller, so it's an overestimate.

Rounded Measurements

The actual value can be bigger or smaller than the rounded value by up to half a unit.

Minimum value: **Rounded value – half a unit**

Maximum value: **Rounded value + half a unit**

ERROR INTERVAL — range of values the actual value could have taken before rounding:

MIN value ≤ Actual value < MAX value

'≤' means the actual value could be equal to the minimum value.

EXAMPLE

The volume of water in a jug is 430 ml to the nearest 10 ml. Find the error interval that contains the actual volume, v.

Minimum volume = 430 − 5 = 425 ml — 5 ml is half of 10 ml.

Maximum volume = 430 + 5 = 435 ml

Error interval is 425 ml ≤ v < 435 ml

Truncated Measurements

TRUNCATING — chopping off decimal places. E.g. 1.283 truncated to 1 d.p. = 1.2.

The actual value can be up to a whole unit bigger, but no smaller than the truncated value.

Minimum value: **Truncated value**

Maximum value: **Truncated value + 1 whole unit**

ERROR INTERVAL — range of values the actual value could have taken before being truncated:

MIN value ≤ Actual value < MAX value

EXAMPLE

Give the error interval for a number, x, that is 5.23 truncated to 2 d.p.

Min value = 5.23

Max value = 5.23 + 0.01 = 5.24

Digit in 2nd d.p. increases by 1.

Interval is 5.23 ≤ x < 5.24

Powers and Roots

Four Rules for Powers

POWERS — numbers multiplied by themselves. $\longrightarrow$

Three to the power 4

$$3^4 = 3 \times 3 \times 3 \times 3$$

1 Powers of ten — the power tells you how many zeros.

$$10^3 = 1000$$

Power of 3

2 Anything to the power 1 is itself. $8^1 = 8$

3 Anything to the power 0 is 1. $12^0 = 1$

4 1 to any power is 1. $1^{27} = 1$

Use a button on your calculator to work out powers — it may look like $x^\blacksquare$ or y^x.

Five Rules for Calculations with Powers

These are only true for powers of the same number.

1 Multiplying — ADD the powers.
$$7^2 \times 7^4 = 7^{2+4} = 7^6$$

2 Dividing — SUBTRACT the powers.
$$5^6 \div 5^3 = 5^{6-3} = 5^3$$

3 Raising one power to another — MULTIPLY the powers.
$$(2^3)^2 = 2^{3 \times 2} = 2^6$$

4 Fractions — apply power to TOP and BOTTOM.
$$\left(\frac{1}{4}\right)^2 = \frac{1^2}{4^2} = \frac{1}{16}$$

5 Negative powers — turn UPSIDE DOWN and make power POSITIVE.
$$5^{-3} = \frac{1}{5^3} = \frac{1}{125}$$

Square Roots

The square root $(\sqrt{\ })$ of a number multiplies by itself to give that number.
E.g. $4 \times 4 = 16$, so $\sqrt{16} = 4$.

Find square roots using what you know about square numbers, or your calculator.

You can also find the negative square root. It's the '−' version of the positive one.

EXAMPLE

81 is a square number.

Find both square roots of 81.

$81 = 9 \times 9$, so positive square root = 9 and negative square root = −9.

Cube Roots

The cube root $(\sqrt[3]{\ })$ of a number multiplies by itself twice to give that number.
E.g. $3 \times 3 \times 3 = 27$, so $\sqrt[3]{27} = 3$.

Find cube roots using what you know about cube numbers, or your calculator.

EXAMPLE

What is $\sqrt[3]{125}$?

125 is a cube number.

$125 = 5 \times 5 \times 5$, so $\sqrt[3]{125} = 5$.

Standard Form

Numbers in Standard Form

STANDARD FORM — used to write very big or very small numbers.

Number between 1 and 10 → $A \times 10^n$ ← Number of places the decimal point moves — positive for big numbers, negative for small numbers

EXAMPLE

What is 24 300 in standard form?

2 4 3 0 0 . 0 — Count how far the decimal point moves to get 2.43

$= 2.43 \times 10^4$ — Big number, so positive n.

EXAMPLE

Express 3.81×10^{-5} as an ordinary number.

Negative n, so small number.

0 0 0 0 0 3 . 8 1 $\times 10^{-5}$

$= 0.0000381$ — Move the decimal point by this many places.

Three Steps to Multiply or Divide

1. Rearrange so the front numbers and powers of 10 are together.

2. Multiply/divide the front numbers. Use power rules to multiply/divide the powers of 10.

3. Put the answer in standard form.

EXAMPLE

Find $(8 \times 10^2) \times (4 \times 10^3)$.
Give your answer in standard form.

$(8 \times 10^2) \times (4 \times 10^3)$

1. $= (8 \times 4) \times (10^2 \times 10^3)$

2. $= 32 \times 10^{2+3}$ — Add powers

$= 32 \times 10^5$ — Not in standard

3. $= 3.2 \times 10 \times 10^5$ form — 32 isn't

$= 3.2 \times 10^6$ between 1 and 10.

Three Steps to Add or Subtract

1. Make sure the powers of 10 are the same.

2. Add/subtract front numbers.

3. Put the answer in standard form if needed.

EXAMPLE

Find $(9.4 \times 10^7) + (6.7 \times 10^6)$.
Give your answer in standard form.

$(9.4 \times 10^7) + (6.7 \times 10^6)$ — Different powers

1. $= (9.4 \times 10^7) + (0.67 \times 10 \times 10^6)$

2. $= (9.4 + 0.67) \times 10^7$

$= 10.07 \times 10^7$ — Not in standard form yet.

3. $= 1.007 \times 10 \times 10^7$

$= 1.007 \times 10^8$

Algebra Basics

Collecting Like Terms

TERM — a collection of numbers, letters and brackets, all multiplied/divided together.

Three steps to collect like terms when you have a mixture of different terms:

1 Put bubbles around each term.

2 Move bubbles so like terms are grouped together.

3 Combine like terms.

EXAMPLE

Simplify:

a) $2x + 5x - 3x$ —— All x terms, so just combine.

$2x + 5x - 3x = 4x$

b) $7a + 2 - 3a + 5$ —— Include the +/− sign in each bubble.

1 $7a$ $+2$ $-3a$ $+5$

2 $= 7a$ $-3a$ $+2$ $+5$

3 $= 4a + 7$

Using Letters

The × signs are left out.

Only q is squared — not p.

Use power rules to divide powers of the same letter.

Notation	Meaning
abc	a × b × c
5a	5 × a
$3\sqrt{a}$	$3 \times \sqrt{a}$
y^4	y × y × y × y
pq^2	p × q × q
$(mn)^2$	m × m × n × n
$\dfrac{a}{b}$	a ÷ b

Powers tell you how many letters are multiplied together.

Brackets mean both m and n are squared.

Multiplying Brackets

Multiply each term inside the bracket by the bit outside the bracket.

Three steps to multiply brackets:

1 Expand each bracket separately.

2 Group like terms together.

3 Simplify the expression.

EXAMPLE

Expand $3x(2x + 1) + 4(3 - 5x)$.

1 $3x(2x + 1) + 4(3 - 5x)$

$= (3x \times 2x) + (3x \times 1)$
$\quad + (4 \times 3) + (4 \times -5x)$

$= 6x^2 + 3x + 12 - 20x$

2 $= 6x^2 + 3x - 20x + 12$

3 $= 6x^2 - 17x + 12$

Double Brackets and Factorising

Using the FOIL Method

To multiply out double brackets:

- Multiply **First** terms of each bracket.
- Multiply **Outside** terms together.
- Multiply **Inside** terms together.
- Multiply **Last** terms of each bracket.

$(m - 6)(m + 4)$

$$= (m \times m) + (m \times 4)$$
$$\quad + (-6 \times m) + (-6 \times 4)$$
$$= m^2 + 4m - 6m - 24$$
$$= m^2 - 2m - 24$$

To multiply **squared brackets**, write them out as double brackets, then use the **FOIL** method as normal.

EXAMPLE

Expand and simplify $(2x - 5)^2$.

$(2x - 5)(2x - 5)$
$= (2x \times 2x) + (2x \times -5) + (-5 \times 2x) + (-5 \times -5)$
$= 4x^2 - 10x - 10x + 25 = 4x^2 - 20x + 25$

Factorising Expressions

FACTORISING — putting brackets back in.

1. Take out the **biggest number** that goes into all terms.

2. Take out the **highest power** of each letter that goes into all terms.

3. Open bracket and fill in what's needed to reproduce the original terms.

4. Check your answer by multiplying out the bracket.

$3b^2 - 9b = 3b(b - 3)$

4. $3b(b - 3) = 3b \times b + 3b \times -3$
$= 3b^2 - 9b$

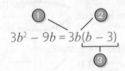

The bits put in front of the bracket are the common factors.

The Difference of Two Squares (D.O.T.S.)

D.O.T.S. — 'one thing squared' take away 'another thing squared'.

Use this rule for factorising: $a^2 - b^2 = (a + b)(a - b)$

The difference? The colour and about 45°...

EXAMPLE

Factorise $x^2 - 25$.
$x^2 - 25 = (x + 5)(x - 5)$

EXAMPLE

Factorise $4p^2 - 9q^2$.
$4p^2 - 9q^2 = (2p + 3q)(2p - 3q)$

Solving Equations

Three Rules for Rearranging Equations

1. Do the same thing to both sides of the equation.

2. Do the opposite operation to get rid of things you don't want.

   + is the opposite of −
   × is the opposite of ÷

3. Keep going until you have a letter on its own.

EXAMPLE

Solve $x - 4 = 9$.

2. The opposite of '−4' is '+4'.

1. $x - 4 + 4 = 9 + 4$
3. $x = 13$

EXAMPLE

Solve $3x = 21$.

1. $3x \div 3 = 21 \div 3$
3. $x = 7$

2. $3x$ means $3 \times x$ — so do the opposite, which is '÷3'.

Two-Step Equations

If there's an x term and a number on the same side of the equation:

1. Add/subtract the number.

2. Multiply/divide to get 'x = ...'.

EXAMPLE

Solve $5x - 3 = 27$.

Add 3 to both sides.

1. $5x - 3 + 3 = 27 + 3$
   $5x = 30$

   Divide both sides by 5.

2. $5x \div 5 = 30 \div 5$
   $x = 6$

When x is on Both Sides

1. Get all the x's on one side of =, and all the numbers on the other.

2. Multiply/divide to get 'x = ...'.

EXAMPLE

Solve $5x + 8 = 2x - 7$.

1. $5x + 8 - 8 = 2x - 7 - 8$
   $5x = 2x - 15$
   $5x - 2x = 2x - 15 - 2x$
   $3x = -15$

2. $3x \div 3 = -15 \div 3$
   $x = -5$

Equations with Brackets

1. Multiply out the brackets.

2. Get all the x's on one side of =, and all the numbers on the other.

3. Multiply/divide to get 'x = ...'.

EXAMPLE

Solve $2(4x + 1) = 5x + 11$.

1. $8x + 2 = 5x + 11$
2. $8x + 2 - 5x = 5x + 11 - 5x$
   $3x + 2 = 11$
   $3x + 2 - 2 = 11 - 2$
3. $3x = 9$
   $x = 3$

Expressions, Formulas and Functions

Definitions

EXPRESSION	A collection of terms — they don't have an '=' sign.	$4x + 5$
EQUATION	An expression that has an '=' sign in it.	$3x - 2 = 7$
FORMULA	A rule that helps you work something out (has an '=' sign).	$F = \frac{9}{5}C + 32$
FUNCTION	An expression that takes an input value, processes it and produces an output value.	'Multiply by 6, then subtract 3'

Putting Numbers into Formulas

① Write out the formula.

② Write it out again, but substitute numbers into the right-hand side.

③ Work it out in stages.

EXAMPLE

The formula for the cost, £C, of hiring a village hall for h hours is £$C = 25h + 100$. Find the cost of hiring the hall for 4 hours.

① £$C = 25h + 100$

② £$C = 25 \times 4 + 100$ — Use BODMAS to work it out in the right order.

③ £$C = 100 + 100 = 200$

So it costs £200 for 4 hours.

Function Machines

Put in a number and follow the steps to get the output.

If you know the output, you can use the function machine in reverse to find the input.

EXAMPLE

This function machine represents the function "multiply by 3 and subtract 2".

a) Find y when $x = 3$.

$3 \xrightarrow{\times 3} 9 \xrightarrow{-2} 7$

b) Find x when $y = 13$.

$13 \xrightarrow{+2} 15 \xrightarrow{\div 3} 5$

Work backwards through the function machine and reverse every step.

Using Formulas and Expressions

Making Expressions

1. Work out what the variable is.

2. Extract all the important information from the question.

3. Make an expression or formula.

4. Use the expression or formula to form an equation and solve to find the variable.
   You won't always be asked to solve for the variable.

EXAMPLE

Abi, Padma and Carl hand out 64 flyers. Padma hands out twice as many as Abi, and Carl hands out 4 more than Padma. How many flyers does Abi hand out?

1. x = the number of flyers Abi hands out
2. Abi = x Padma = $2x$ Carl = $2x + 4$
3. Total = $x + 2x + (2x + 4) = 5x + 4$
4. $5x + 4 = 64$
   $5x = 60$, so $x = 12$
   So Abi hands out 12 flyers.

Using Shape Properties

Follow the same steps as above. Use things like side lengths, areas or perimeters to form the expressions.

EXAMPLE

For the shapes below, the perimeter of the square is the same as the perimeter of the triangle. Find the value of x.

Triangle perimeter = $(4x + 1) + (2x + 3) + 2x = 8x + 4$

Square perimeter = $4(x + 5) = 4x + 20$

$8x + 4 = 4x + 20$ ⟵ The perimeters are
$4x = 16$ the same, so form an
$x = 4$ equation and solve.

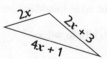

$x + 5$

Three Rules for Rearranging Formulas

1. Do the same thing to both sides of the formula.

2. Do the opposite operation to get rid of things you don't want.
   + is the opposite of −
   × is the opposite of ÷

3. Keep going until you have the letter you want on its own.

EXAMPLE

Rearrange $q = \dfrac{7p - 3}{5}$ to make p the subject of the formula.

1. $q \times 5 = \dfrac{7p - 3}{5} \times 5$
   $5q = 7p - 3$
   $5q + 3 = 7p - 3 + 3$
   $5q + 3 = 7p$
   $(5q + 3) \div 7 = 7p \div 7$
3. $p = \dfrac{5q + 3}{7}$

Sequences

Number and Shape Sequences

To find the rule for a sequence, work out how to get from one term to the next.

LINEAR SEQUENCES — adding
or subtracting the same number:

$$-7 \quad -7 \quad -7$$
$$31 \quad 24 \quad 17 \quad 10 \ldots$$
Rule: Subtract 7 from the previous term

GEOMETRIC SEQUENCES — multiplying
or dividing by the same number:

$$\div 2 \quad \div 2 \quad \div 2$$
$$72 \quad 36 \quad 18 \quad 9 \ldots$$
Rule: Divide previous term by 2

Pattern 1   Pattern 2   Pattern 3
Rule: Add 2 circles to previous pattern

Pattern 1   Pattern 2   Pattern 3
Rule: Multiply number of squares by 3

nth Term of Linear Sequences

NTH TERM — a rule that gives the terms in a
sequence when you put in different 'n' values.

1. Find the common difference —
   this is what you multiply n by.

2. Work out what to add/subtract.

3. Put both bits together.

EXAMPLE

Find the nth term of the
sequence 7, 11, 15, 19 ...

1. $11 - 7 = 4$, $15 - 11 = 4$, etc.
   So common difference = 4

2. For n = 1, 4n = 4. $7 - 4 = 3$,
   so 3 is added to each term.

3. So nth term is $4n + 3$

Deciding if a Term is in a Sequence

Set nth term rule equal to the number
and solve for n. The term is in the
sequence if n is a whole number.

EXAMPLE

Is 37 a term in the sequence
with the nth term $6n - 1$?

$$6n - 1 = 37$$
$$6n = 38$$
$$n = 6.333\ldots$$

So 37 is not in the sequence.

Other Types of Sequences

QUADRATIC SEQUENCE —
the number you add/subtract changes
by the same amount each time.

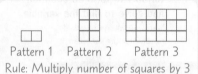

Terms in this
sequence are
the triangular
numbers.

FIBONACCI-TYPE SEQUENCE —
add previous two terms together.

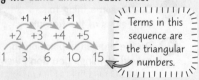

Inequalities and Quadratic Equations

Solving Inequalities

> means GREATER THAN

< means LESS THAN

≥ means GREATER THAN OR EQUAL TO

≤ means LESS THAN OR EQUAL TO

To represent inequalities on number lines:

- Use a closed circle (●) for ≤ or ≥
- Use an open circle (○) for < or >

Solve inequalities like equations — but if you multiply/divide by a negative number, flip the inequality sign.

EXAMPLE

Show $-2 \leq x < 5$ on the number line below.

$$+\!\!+\!\!+\!\!+\!\!+\!\!+\!\!+\!\!+\!\!+\!\!+\!\!+\!\!+\!\!+$$
$$-4\;-3\;-2\;-1\;0\;\;1\;\;2\;\;3\;\;4\;\;5\;\;6\;\;7$$

This inequality means "x is greater than or equal to -2 and less than 5".

EXAMPLE

Solve $3 - 5x \leq 18$.

$3 - 5x \leq 18$

$-5x \leq 18 - 3$

$-5x \leq 15$ — Divided by a negative number,

$x \geq -3$ — so flip the sign.

Solving Quadratic Equations

Standard form of a quadratic equation:

$$x^2 + bx + c = 0$$

(b and c can be any number)

To FACTORISE — put it into two brackets.

To SOLVE — find the values of x that make each bracket equal to 0.

Six steps to solve quadratics:

1. Rearrange to $x^2 + bx + c = 0$.

2. Write two brackets: (x   )(x   ) = 0

3. Find two numbers that multiply to give 'c' AND add/subtract to give 'b'.

4. Fill in + or − signs.

5. Check by expanding brackets.

6. Solve the equation.

EXAMPLE

Solve $x^2 - 6x = -8$.

1. $x^2 - 6x + 8 = 0$

2. $(x \quad)(x \quad) = 0$

3. Factor pairs of 8: 1×8 and 2×4

   $1 + 8 = 9$ and $8 - 1 = 7$
   $2 + 4 = 6$ and $4 - 2 = 2$

   So the numbers are 2 and 4.

4. $(x - 2)(x - 4) = 0$

5. $(x - 2)(x - 4)$
   $= x^2 - 4x - 2x + 8$
   $= x^2 - 6x + 8$

6. $(x - 2) = 0 \implies x = 2$
   $(x - 4) = 0 \implies x = 4$

Work out which signs you need by looking at c. If c is positive, the signs will be the same. If c is negative, the signs will be different.

20

Simultaneous Equations and Proof

Solving Simultaneous Equations

Six steps to solve them:

1 Rearrange into the form $ax + by = c$.

2 Match up the coefficients for one of the variables.

3 Add or subtract to get rid of a variable.

4 Solve the equation.

5 Substitute the value back into one of the original equations.

6 Check your answer works.

EXAMPLE

Solve the simultaneous equations
$5 - 2x = 3y$ and $5x + 4 = -2y$

1 $2x + 3y = 5$ (1)   Label your
$5x + 2y = -4$ (2)   equations.

2 (1) × 5: $10x + 15y = 25$ (3)
(2) × 2: $10x + 4y = -8$ (4)

3 (3) − (4): $0x + 11y = 33$
                       $25 - -8 = 33$

4 $11y = 33 \Rightarrow y = 3$

5 Sub $y = 3$ into (1): $2x + (3 \times 3) = 5$
$\Rightarrow 2x = 5 - 9 \Rightarrow 2x = -4 \Rightarrow x = -2$

6 Sub x and y into (2):
$(5 \times -2) + (2 \times 3) = -10 + 6 = -4$
So the solution is $x = -2$, $y = 3$

Proof

To show that something is **false**, find an example that **doesn't** work.

proof

It's in the pudding.

EXAMPLE

Find an example to show that this statement is false:
"The sum of two square numbers is always odd."
$1 + 4 = 5$ (odd) $4 + 9 = 13$ (odd) $1 + 9 = 10$ (even), so the statement is false.

To show that something is **true**, you might need to rearrange to show
two things are the same, or show something is a multiple of a number.

EXAMPLE

Prove $(n - 4)^2 - (n + 1)^2 \equiv -5(2n - 3)$.

$(n - 4)^2 - (n + 1)^2$
$\equiv (n^2 - 8n + 16) - (n^2 + 2n + 1)$
$\equiv n^2 - 8n + 16 - n^2 - 2n - 1$
$\equiv -10n + 15$
$\equiv -5(2n - 3)$

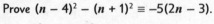 The identity symbol '$\equiv$' means this is true for all values of n.

EXAMPLE

$y = 2(6x + 4) + 3(3x - 5) + 1$
Show y is a multiple of 3
when x is a whole number.

$y = 2(6x + 4) + 3(3x - 5) + 1$
$= 12x + 8 + 9x - 15 + 1$
$= 21x - 6 = 3(7x - 2)$
y can be written as 3 × something
(where the something is $7x - 2$),
so it is a multiple of 3.

Section 2 — Algebra

Coordinates and Straight Lines

Coordinates and Quadrants

Coordinates are written as: **(x, y)**

x is the horizontal axis

y is the vertical axis

To read coordinates, go along then up (x-coordinate then y-coordinate).

The x- and y-coordinates can be positive or negative, depending on which of the four quadrants (regions) you're in:

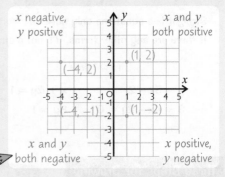

x negative, y positive

x and y both positive

$(-4, 2)$ $(1, 2)$

$(-4, -1)$ $(1, -2)$

x and y both negative

x positive, y negative

Midpoint of a Line

MIDPOINT OF A LINE SEGMENT — point exactly halfway between the line's endpoints.

Three steps to find the midpoint:

1. Find the average of the x-coordinates.

2. Find the average of the y-coordinates.

3. Put them in brackets.

EXAMPLE

Point A has coordinates $(-8, 2)$ and Point B has coordinates $(6, 10)$. Find the coordinates of the midpoint of AB.

1. $\dfrac{-8 + 6}{2} = \dfrac{-2}{2} = -1$ 2. $\dfrac{2 + 10}{2} = \dfrac{12}{2} = 6$

3. Coordinates of midpoint: $(-1, 6)$

Straight-Line Equations

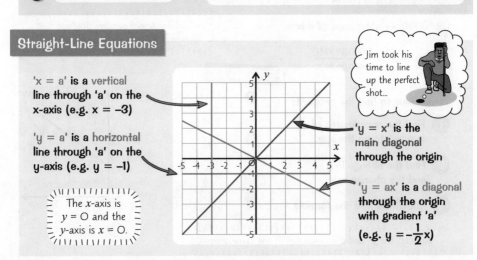

'x = a' is a vertical line through 'a' on the x-axis (e.g. $x = -3$)

'y = a' is a horizontal line through 'a' on the y-axis (e.g. $y = -1$)

The x-axis is $y = 0$ and the y-axis is $x = 0$.

Jim took his time to line up the perfect shot...

'y = x' is the main diagonal through the origin

'y = ax' is a diagonal through the origin with gradient 'a' (e.g. $y = -\frac{1}{2}x$)

Drawing Straight-Line Graphs

Spotting Straight-Line Equations

Straight-line equations only have an x-term, a y-term and a number term.
If there are any other terms, it's not a straight line.

Straight lines:		NOT straight lines:	
$y = 5x - 2$	$x + 2y = 1$	$y = 3x^2 + 1$	$xy = 1$
$3 + 4x - 2y = 0$	$8y = 1$	$x^2 + y^2 = 3$	$5 = 3y - \frac{2}{x}$

Three Steps for Drawing

1 Draw a table with three values of x.

2 Put the x-values into the equation and work out the y-values.

3 Plot the points and draw a straight line through them.

EXAMPLE

Draw the graph $y = -2x + 3$ **3** for values of x from 0 to 4.

1 x	0	2	4
2 y	3	−1	−5

E.g. when $x = 2$,
$y = -2(2) + 3$
$= -4 + 3 = -1$

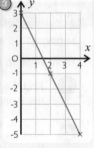

Finding the Gradient

GRADIENT — steepness of a line.

$$\text{Gradient} = \frac{\text{change in y}}{\text{change in x}}$$

Uphill slope = positive gradient
Downhill slope = negative gradient

Three steps to find the gradient:

1 Find the coordinates of two points on the line.

2 Find the change in y and the change in x.

3 Substitute into the formula.

EXAMPLE

1 A: (1, 3)   B: (5, 6)

2 Change in y: $6 - 3 = 3$
Change in x: $5 - 1 = 4$

3 Gradient $= \frac{3}{4} = 0.75$

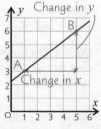

Subtract the y- and x-coordinates in the same order.

$y = mx + c$

Equation of a Straight Line

General equation for a straight-line graph:

$$y = mx + c$$

c = y-intercept (where the graph crosses the y-axis)

m = gradient

Rearrange other straight-line equations into this form:

$3x - y = 5 \implies y = 3x - 5$

$7x + y - 2 = 0 \implies y = -7x + 2$

Parallel lines have the same gradient, so they have the same value of m:

$y = 3x + 2$ has gradient 3 and y-intercept 2
$y = 3x - 4$ has gradient 3 and y-intercept -4

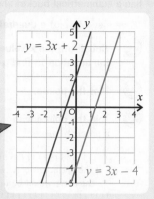

Three Steps to Find the Equation

1. Use any two points on the line to find the gradient, 'm'.

2. Read off the y-intercept, 'c'.

3. Write equation as $y = mx + c$.

EXAMPLE

Find the equation of this line in the form $y = mx + c$.

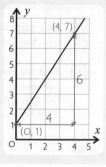

1. $m = \dfrac{6}{4} = \dfrac{3}{2}$

2. $c = 1$

3. $y = \dfrac{3}{2}x + 1$

Equation of a Line Through Two Points

1. Use both points to find gradient.

2. Substitute one point into $y = mx + c$.

3. Rearrange to find 'c'.

4. Write equation as $y = mx + c$.

EXAMPLE

Find the equation of the straight line that passes through $(-2, 12)$ and $(4, -6)$.

1. $m = \dfrac{-6 - 12}{4 - (-2)} = \dfrac{-18}{6} = -3$

2. Sub in $(4, -6)$:
   $-6 = -3(4) + c \implies -6 = -12 + c$

3. $c = -6 + 12 = 6$

4. $y = -3x + 6$

Quadratic Graphs

Quadratic Graphs

A quadratic graph (y = anything with x^2, but no higher powers) has a symmetrical bucket shape.

Three steps to plot a quadratic graph:

① Substitute the x-values into the equation to find y-values.

② Plot the points.

③ Join the points with a smooth curve.

‌⎧⎭⎫ If the coefficient of x^2 were negative, the curve would be upside down. ⎫⎭⎧

EXAMPLE

Plot the graph of $y = x^2 + 2x - 1$.

x	−4	−3	−2	−1	0	1	2
y	7	2	−1	−2	−1	2	7

E.g. $y = (-4)^2 + 2(-4) - 1$
$= 16 - 8 - 1 = 7$

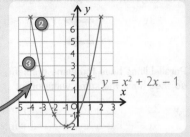

$y = x^2 + 2x - 1$

Three Steps to Find the Turning Point

① Pick two points on the curve with the same y-value.

② Find the number halfway between the x-coordinates. This is the x-coordinate of the turning point.

③ Put x back into the equation to find y.

EXAMPLE

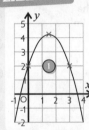

Find the turning point of $y = -x^2 + 3x + 2$.

② Halfway between $x = 0$ and $x = 3$ is 1.5.

③ $y = -(1.5)^2 + 3(1.5) + 2$
$= -2.25 + 4.5 + 2 = 4.25$

Turning point: (1.5, 4.25)

Solving Quadratic Equations

ROOTS — x-values where a curve crosses the x-axis. These are solutions to 'equation' = 0.

To find roots from a graph, read off the values where the curve crosses the x-axis.

EXAMPLE

Use the graph to solve $2x^2 + 4x = 0$.

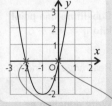

Solutions (roots) are $x = -2$ and $x = 0$.

Harder Graphs

Cubic Graphs

A cubic graph ($y =$ anything with x^3, but no higher powers) has a wiggle in the middle.

$+x^3$ graphs go up from bottom left: $-x^3$ graphs go down from top left:

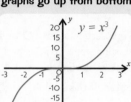

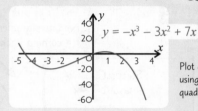

Plot cubic graphs using the steps for quadratic graphs.

Reciprocal Graphs

Equation: $$y = \frac{1}{x}$$

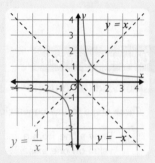

- Graphs have two symmetrical curves — one in the top right and one in the bottom left quadrant.
- Two halves of graph don't touch.
- Curves never touch the axes.
- Symmetrical about lines $y = x$ and $y = -x$.

Solving Simultaneous Equations

EXAMPLE

By plotting the graphs, solve the simultaneous equations $y = -2x$ and $y = x - 3$.

① Plot both equations on a graph.

② Read off the x- and y-values where the two lines intersect.

To find the solution to an equation (e.g. $-2x = x - 3$), split it into two 'y =' curves ($y = -2x$ and $y = x - 3$). Then follow the steps above.

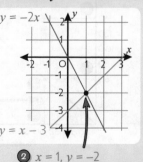

② $x = 1$, $y = -2$

Distance-Time and Conversion Graphs

Distance-Time Graphs

DISTANCE-TIME GRAPHS — show distance travelled against time.

Distance from the starting point goes on the vertical axis and
time goes on the horizontal axis. The gradient gives the speed.

EXAMPLE

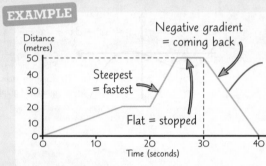

Negative gradient = coming back

Steepest = fastest

Flat = stopped

Final section starts 50 m from starting point at 30 s and ends back at starting point at 40 s.

Speed of this section

$$= \frac{0 - 50}{40 - 30} = \frac{-50}{10} = -5 \text{ m/s},$$

so coming back at 5 m/s.

Conversion Graphs

CONVERSION GRAPHS — show how to convert between units.

Three steps to use conversion graphs:

1 Draw a line from a value on one axis.

2 When you reach the conversion line, go to the other axis.

3 Read off the value from this axis.

EXAMPLE

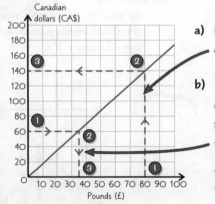

a) **How many Canadian dollars is £80?**

Go up from £80: £80 = CA$140

b) **How many pounds is CA$600?**

CA$600 isn't on the graph, so pick an easy number to use instead:

CA$60 = £35

Multiply to work out CA$600:

CA$600 = £35 × 10 = £350

Real-Life Graphs and Rate of Change

Money Graphs

EXAMPLE

This graph shows the amount a company charges to ship an order.

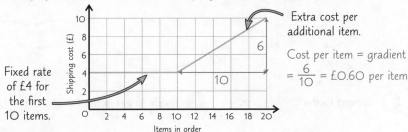

Fixed rate of £4 for the first 10 items.

Extra cost per additional item.

Cost per item = gradient
$= \frac{6}{10} = $ £0.60 per item

Rate of Change

RATE OF CHANGE — how quickly something is changing.
- **Rate of change = gradient.**
- **Steeper gradient = faster rate of change.**
- **Units: y-axis unit PER x-axis unit.**

To find the rate of change, work out the gradient of the line, then add the units.

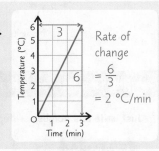

Rate of change
$= \frac{6}{3}$
$= 2 \,°C/min$

Changes with Time

EXAMPLE

Three jars are filled with sand at a constant rate. These graphs show the height of sand in each jar.

Height rises faster when the jar is narrower:

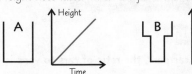

The jar has a constant width, so the height rises at a constant rate.

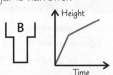

The jar is narrow then wide, so the height rises quickly then slowly.

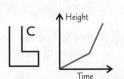

The jar is wide then narrow, so the height rises slowly then quickly.

Ratios

Four Ways to Simplify Ratios

1 Divide all numbers by the same thing.

2 Multiply to get rid of fractions **and** decimals.

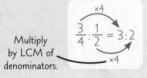

Multiply by LCM of denominators.

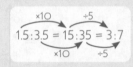

3 Convert to the smaller unit.

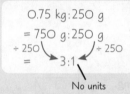

No units

4 Divide to get in the form 1:n or n:1.

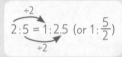

The fraction button on your calculator can be used to help simplify ratios.

Writing One Part as a Fraction of Another

Just write one number on top of the other.

 :

My sweets   :   Your sweets

EXAMPLE

Cats and dogs are in the ratio 3:2.

There are $\frac{3}{2}$ as many cats as dogs, or there are $\frac{2}{3}$ as many dogs as cats.

Two Steps to Write One Part as a Fraction of the Total

1 Add to find the total number of parts.

2 Write the part you want over the total.

EXAMPLE

In a car park, the ratio of cars to vans is 8:3.

1 There are 8 + 3 = 11 parts in total.

2 So $\frac{8}{11}$ are cars and $\frac{3}{11}$ are vans.

More Ratios

Three Steps to Scale Up Ratios

1 Work out what one side of the ratio is multiplied by to get its actual value.

2 Multiply the other side by this number.

3 Add the two sides to find the total (if the question asks you to).

The two sides of a ratio are always in direct proportion.

EXAMPLE

A theatre audience is made up of adults and children in the ratio 3:5. There are 120 adults. How many people are there in the audience in total?

1 ×40   3:5   ×40 **2**
120:200

So there are 200 children.

3 120 + 200 = 320 people

Part:Whole Ratios

PART:WHOLE RATIO — left-hand side of ratio included in right-hand side.

part:part ➡ part:whole

Add the parts to find the whole.

EXAMPLE

Fiction and non-fiction books are in the ratio 3:7.
Total parts = 3 + 7 = 10
Ratio of fiction to total books is 3:10.
Ratio of non-fiction to total books is 7:10.

part:whole ➡ part:part

Subtract the part you know from the whole to find the other part.

EXAMPLE

Kei has red and grey socks. The ratio of red socks to all of his socks is 5:8.

8 − 5 = 3 parts are grey. So ratio of red socks to grey socks is 5:3.

Three Steps for Proportional Division

1 Add up the parts.

2 Divide to find one part.

3 Multiply to find the amounts.

EXAMPLE

1200 g of flour is used to make cakes, pastry and bread in the ratio 8:7:9. How much flour is used to make pastry?

1 8 + 7 + 9 = 24 parts
2 1 part = 1200 g ÷ 24 = 50 g
3 7 parts = 7 × 50 g = 350 g

Direct Proportion

Two Steps for Direct Proportion

DIRECT PROPORTION — two amounts increase or decrease together, at the same rate.

1 Divide to find the amount for one thing.

2 Multiply to find the amount for the number of things you want.

EXAMPLE

3 footballs cost £29.70.
How much do 7 footballs cost?

1 1 football costs
£29.70 ÷ 3 = £9.90

2 7 footballs cost
£9.90 × 7 = £69.30

Two Steps for Scaling Recipes

1 Divide to find the amount for one person.

2 Multiply to find the amount for the number of people you want.

EXAMPLE

A smoothie recipe for 6 people uses 900 ml of apple juice. How much apple juice is needed to make smoothies for 4 people?

1 For 1 person you need
900 ml ÷ 6 = 150 ml of apple juice

2 For 4 people you need
150 ml × 4 = 600 ml of apple juice

Two Steps to Find the Best Buy

1 For each item, divide amount by price in pence to get amount per penny.

2 Compare amounts per penny to find the best value.

You can also divide the price by the amount (length, mass, etc.) to get the cost per unit. A smaller cost per unit means better value.

EXAMPLE

Some wrapping paper comes in rolls of two lengths, as shown.

Which roll is better value for money?

5 m roll £4   2 m roll £2.50

1 5 m = 500 cm ——— It's easier if you convert m to cm.
£4 = 400p ——— Convert £ to p.
500 cm ÷ 400p = 1.25 cm per penny.

2 m = 200 cm
£2.50 = 250p
200 cm ÷ 250p = 0.8 cm per penny.

2 The 5 m roll is better value as you get more paper per penny. ——— More per penny means better value for money.

Direct and Inverse Proportion

Graphing Direct Proportion

Two things in direct proportion make a straight-line graph.

- Line goes through the **origin**.

- All direct proportions can be written as an **equation** of the form:

$$y = Ax$$ A is a number.

- To find A, substitute given values into the equation.

EXAMPLE

The amount of paint needed to paint a wall is directly proportional to its area. 12 litres of paint are needed for an area of 100 m².

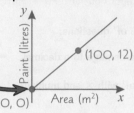

12 = A × 100, so A = 12 ÷ 100 = 0.12
So $y = 0.12x$

Two Steps for Inverse Proportion

INVERSE PROPORTION — one amount increases as the other decreases, at the same rate. E.g. when one amount doubles, the other halves.

1 Multiply to find the amount for one thing.

2 Divide to find the amount for the number of things you want.

EXAMPLE

It takes two people 5 minutes to peel 30 potatoes. How long would it take five people to peel 30 potatoes at the same rate?

1 30 potatoes would take one person
5 × 2 = 10 minutes

2 Five people would take
10 ÷ 5 = 2 minutes

Graphing Inverse Proportion

Two things in inverse proportion make a graph that curves down from left to right.

- Curve **doesn't** go through the **origin**.

- All inverse proportions can be written as an **equation** of the form:

$$y = \frac{A}{x}$$ A is a number.

- To find A, substitute given values into the equation.

EXAMPLE

y is inversely proportional to x.
When $x = 2$, $y = 4$.

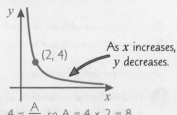

As x increases, y decreases.

$4 = \dfrac{A}{2}$, so A = 4 × 2 = 8

So $y = \dfrac{8}{x}$

Percentages

Finding Percentages of Amounts

'Per cent' means 'out of 100'.

E.g. 30% means '30 out of 100' = $\frac{30}{100}$ = 0.3

To find 10%, divide by 10.
To find 5%, find 10% then divide by 2. To find 1%, divide by 100.

Two steps for '% of' questions:

1. Change percentage to a decimal.

2. Replace 'of' with × and multiply.

EXAMPLE

Find 45% of 80.

1. 45% = 0.45

2. 0.45 × 80 = 36

x as a Percentage of y

1. Divide x by y.

2. Multiply by 100.

EXAMPLE

Write 30 as a percentage of 250.

1. $\frac{30}{250} = \frac{3}{25}$ — Simplify fraction first if you don't have a calculator.

2. $\frac{3}{25}$ × 100 = 12%

Two Methods for Percentage Change

Find Percentage **then** Add or Subtract:

1. Find % of original amount.

2. Add to/subtract from original value.

The Multiplier **Method:**

MULTIPLIER — decimal you multiply original value by to increase/decrease it by a %.

% increase — multiplier is greater than 1
% decrease — multiplier is less than 1

Two steps for using multipliers:

1. Find multiplier — write % change as a decimal and add to/subtract from 1.

2. Multiply original value by multiplier.

EXAMPLE

Increase £25 by 20%.

1. 20% of £25
   = 0.2 × £25
   = £5 — It's an increase, so add.

2. £25 + £5 = £30

EXAMPLE

A scarf originally cost £7.50. Its price is reduced by 12%. Find the new price.

1. 12% = 0.12
   Multiplier for 12% decrease
   = 1 − 0.12 = 0.88

2. New price of scarf
   = £7.50 × 0.88 = £6.60

More Percentages

Simple Interest

SIMPLE INTEREST — a % of the original value is paid at regular intervals (e.g. every year). The amount of interest doesn't change.

Three steps for simple interest questions:

1. Find the interest earned each time.

2. Multiply by the number of intervals.

3. Add to original value (if needed).

EXAMPLE

Lila puts £2500 in a savings account that pays 2% simple interest each year. How much will be in the account after 5 years?

1. 2% of £2500
   = 0.02 × £2500 = £50

2. 5 × £50 = £250 — Total interest earned

3. £2500 + £250 = £2750

Finding the Percentage Change

'Change' = increase, decrease, profit, loss, etc.

$$\text{Percentage change} = \frac{\text{change}}{\text{original}} \times 100$$

Two steps to find the percentage change:

1. Find the change between the two amounts.

2. Put values into the formula.

EXAMPLE

A car was bought for £11 500. It is sold for £8855. Find the percentage loss.

1. Loss = £11 500 − £8855
   = £2645

2. % loss = $\frac{2645}{11\ 500} \times 100$
   = 0.23 × 100 = 23%

Three Steps to Find the Original Value

1. Write the amount as a percentage of the original value.

2. Divide to find 1% of original value.

3. Multiply by 100 to find the original value (100%).

Meg's interest in percentages simply wasn't increasing.

EXAMPLE

A village has a population of 960. The population of the village has increased by 20% since 2016. What was the population in 2016?

1. 960 = 120%

2. 960 ÷ 120 = 120% ÷ 120
   8 = 1%

3. 8 × 100 = 1% × 100
   800 = 100%

So the population in 2016 was 800.

Compound Growth and Units

Compound Growth and Decay

COMPOUND GROWTH/DECAY — the amount added on/taken away changes each time (it's a % of the new amount, rather than the original).

> Depreciation is an example of compound decay.

Formula for compound growth and decay:

Amount after n years/days/hours etc. ⟶ $N = N_0 \times (\text{multiplier})^n$ ⟵ Number of years/days/hours etc.

Initial amount ⟶ | % change multiplier

EXAMPLE

Callum invests £4800 in a savings account that pays 2% compound interest each year. How much will there be in the account after 3 years?

N_0 = £4800, multiplier = 1 + 0.02 = 1.02, n = 3

Amount after 3 years = £4800 × 1.02^3

= £5093.80 (to the nearest penny)

> You could also work this out by finding the amount each year. E.g. after 1 year there's £4800 × 1.02 = £4896, after 2 years there's £4896 × 1.02 = £4993.92, etc.

Converting Units

Metric conversions:

1 cm = 10 mm	1 tonne = 1000 kg
1 m = 100 cm	1 litre = 1000 ml
1 km = 1000 m	1 litre = 1000 cm^3
1 kg = 1000 g	1 cm^3 = 1 ml

Three steps for converting units:

1. **Find** conversion factor.
2. **Multiply AND divide** by it.
3. **Choose** sensible answer.

> Think which unit there should be more of.

For **metric-imperial conversions**, conversion factors will be given.

EXAMPLE

Thandi runs 3500 m.
How far does she run in km?

1. 1 km = 1000 m, so conversion factor = 1000
2. ~~3500 × 1000 = 3 500 000~~
   3500 ÷ 1000 = 3.5 — Cross out incorrect working.
3. 3500 m = 3.5 km — Add units.

EXAMPLE

A tank holds 18 gallons of fuel. Given 1 gallon ≈ 4.5 litres, how much fuel can the tank hold in litres?

1. Conversion factor = 4.5
2. 18 × 4.5 = 81
   ~~18 ÷ 4.5 = 4~~
3. 18 gallons ≈ 81 litres

Units — Area, Volume and Time

Three Steps for Converting Areas

1. Find the conversion factor for converting length.
2. Multiply AND divide by it twice.
3. Choose the sensible answer.

1. $1 \text{ m} = 100 \text{ cm}$
2. $5 \text{ cm}^2 = 5 \times 100 \times 100$
   $= 50\,000 \text{ m}^2$
   $5 \text{ cm}^2 = 5 \div 100 \div 100$
   $= 0.0005 \text{ m}^2$ 3.

Three Steps for Converting Volumes

1. Find the conversion factor for converting length.
2. Multiply AND divide by it three times.
3. Choose the sensible answer.

1. $1 \text{ cm} = 10 \text{ mm}$
2. $2 \text{ cm}^3 = 2 \times 10 \times 10 \times 10$
   $= 2000 \text{ mm}^3$ 3.
   $2 \text{ cm}^3 = 2 \div 10 \div 10 \div 10$
   $= 0.002 \text{ mm}^3$

Converting Time Units

Standard time unit conversions:

1 day = 24 hours
1 hour = 60 minutes
1 minute = 60 seconds

EXAMPLE

Write 4800 seconds in hours and minutes.
4800 seconds = 4800 ÷ 60 = 80 minutes
80 minutes = 80 ÷ 60 = 1 full hour
and 80 − 60 = 20 minutes ——— Split into stages
So 4800 seconds = 1 hour 20 minutes

Time Calculations

1. Split time interval into stages.
2. Convert each stage to the same units (if needed).
3. Add to get total time.

EXAMPLE

Rowan starts a walk at 10.30 am and finishes at 2.15 pm. How many minutes does his walk last?
1. 10.30 am ⟶ 11 am ⟶ 2 pm ⟶ 2.15 pm
   30 mins 3 hours 15 mins
2. 3 hours = 3 × 60 = 180 minutes
3. 30 + 180 + 15 = 225 minutes

Reading Timetables

Here's part of a bus timetable. Read along rows and up/down columns to find answers.

First bus from Town Centre gets to Park Avenue at 10:03.

Town Centre	09 50	10 10	10 30
Main Square	09 55	10 15	10 35
Park Avenue	10 03	10 23	10 43

Town Centre to Park Avenue takes 13 minutes.

+5
+8

10:23 bus at Park Avenue leaves Town Centre at 10:10.

Section 4 — Ratio, Proportion and Rates of Change

Speed, Density and Pressure

Speed, Time and Distance

$$\text{SPEED} = \frac{\text{DISTANCE}}{\text{TIME}}$$

$$\text{TIME} = \frac{\text{DISTANCE}}{\text{SPEED}}$$

$$\text{DISTANCE} = \text{SPEED} \times \text{TIME}$$

Units of speed: distance travelled per unit time, e.g. km/h, m/s

EXAMPLE

A fox walks 13.5 km at an average speed of 4.5 km/h. How long does the fox walk for?

Write down the formula:
$$\text{Time} = \frac{\text{distance}}{\text{speed}}$$

Put in the numbers:
$$= \frac{13.5}{4.5}$$

Add the units:
$$= 3 \text{ hours}$$

In a formula triangle, cover what you want and write what's left.

Density, Volume and Mass

$$\text{DENSITY} = \frac{\text{MASS}}{\text{VOLUME}}$$

$$\text{VOLUME} = \frac{\text{MASS}}{\text{DENSITY}}$$

$$\text{MASS} = \text{DENSITY} \times \text{VOLUME}$$

Units of density: mass per unit volume, e.g. kg/m³, g/cm³

Pressure, Area and Force

$$\text{PRESSURE} = \frac{\text{FORCE}}{\text{AREA}}$$

$$\text{AREA} = \frac{\text{FORCE}}{\text{PRESSURE}}$$

$$\text{FORCE} = \text{PRESSURE} \times \text{AREA}$$

Units of pressure: force per unit area, e.g. N/m² (or pascals)

Converting Units of Speed, Density and Pressure

Units of speed, density and pressure are made up of two measures.

Convert each measure separately.

Work out the conversion factor first if you need to.

EXAMPLE

Convert 300 m/s to km/h.

300 m/s to km/s:

1 km = 1000 m, so conversion factor = 1000

~~300 × 1000 = 300 000~~, 300 ÷ 1000 = 0.3

So 300 m/s = 0.3 km/s

0.3 km/s to km/h:

1 h = 60 mins and 1 min = 60 s,

so conversion factor = 60 × 60 = 3600

0.3 × 3600 = 1080, ~~0.3 ÷ 3600 = 0.000083...~~

So 300 m/s = 0.3 km/s = 1080 km/h

Properties of 2D Shapes

Line Symmetry

LINE SYMMETRY — where the two parts of a shape on either side of a mirror line fold exactly together.

   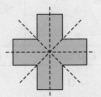

| 1 line of symmetry | 2 lines of symmetry | 3 lines of symmetry | 4 lines of symmetry | 5 lines of symmetry |

Rotational Symmetry

ROTATIONAL SYMMETRY — where a shape looks exactly the same after you rotate it into different positions.

ORDER OF ROTATIONAL SYMMETRY — how many different positions look the same.

| Order 1 | Order 2 | Order 3 | Order 4 |

Same as no rotational symmetry.

Regular Polygons

Equilateral triangles and squares are regular polygons.

REGULAR POLYGON — all sides and angles are the same.

Name	Pentagon	Hexagon	Heptagon	Octagon	Nonagon	Decagon
No. of sides	5	6	7	8	9	10

Regular polygons have the same number of lines of symmetry as the number of sides. Their order of rotational symmetry is also the same.

Triangles and Quadrilaterals

Four Types of Triangles

All sides and angles are different.

Dashes show sides of the same length.

60°

90°

Type	Equilateral	Isosceles	Right-angled	Scalene
Lines of symmetry	3	1	0 (unless isosceles)	0
Rotational symmetry	Order 3	None	None	None

Six Types of Quadrilaterals

SQUARE

- 4 equal angles of 90°
- 4 lines of symmetry
- Rotational symmetry order 4

RECTANGLE

- 4 equal angles of 90°
- 2 lines of symmetry
- Rotational symmetry order 2

RHOMBUS

Arrows show that sides are parallel. Arcs show that angles are equal.

- 4 equal sides (opposites are parallel)
- 2 pairs of equal angles
- 2 lines of symmetry
- Rotational symmetry order 2

PARALLELOGRAM

- 2 pairs of equal sides (sides in each pair are parallel)
- 2 pairs of equal angles
- No lines of symmetry
- Rotational symmetry order 2

TRAPEZIUM

- 1 pair of parallel sides
- No lines of symmetry (unless isosceles)
- No rotational symmetry

KITE

- 2 pairs of equal sides
- 1 pair of equal angles
- 1 line of symmetry
- No rotational symmetry

Congruent and Similar Shapes

Congruent Shapes

CONGRUENT — same shape and same size.

EXAMPLE Which of these shapes are congruent?

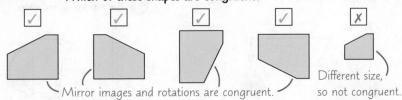

Mirror images and rotations are congruent.

Different size, so not congruent.

Four Conditions for Congruent Triangles

Condition	1 SSS	2 ASA	3 SAS	4 RHS
Description	three sides the same	two angles and corresponding side match up	two sides and angle between them match up	right angle, hypotenuse and another side all match up
Diagrams	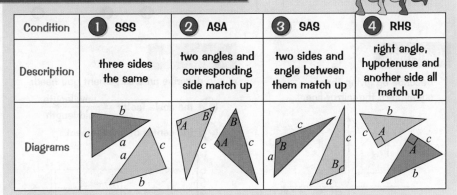			

Similar Shapes

SIMILAR — same shape and different size.

If you know two shapes are similar, work out the scale factor to find any missing lengths.

Three conditions for similar triangles:

1 All angles match up.

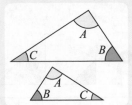

2 All sides are proportional.

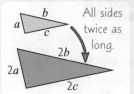

All sides twice as long.

3 Two sides proportional and the angle between them is the same.

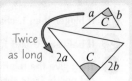

Twice as long

The Four Transformations

Translation

Amount a shape moves is given by $\begin{pmatrix} x \\ y \end{pmatrix}$.

x = horizontal movement (+ right, − left)
y = vertical movement (+ up, − down)

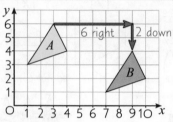

Translation from A to B: $\begin{pmatrix} 6 \\ -2 \end{pmatrix}$

Rotation

To describe a rotation you need:

1 the angle   **2** the direction

3 the centre of rotation

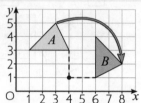

Rotation from A to B:
90° clockwise about (4, 1)
1   **2**   **3**

Reflection

Describe by giving the
equation of the mirror line.

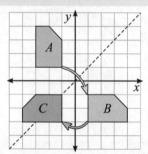

B is a reflection of A in $y = x$
C is a reflection of B in the y-axis

Enlargement

To describe an enlargement you need:

1 the scale factor $= \dfrac{\text{new length}}{\text{old length}}$

2 the centre of enlargement

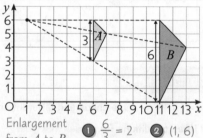

Enlargement
from A to B: **1** $\dfrac{6}{3} = 2$ **2** (1, 6)

Three Facts about Scale Factors

1 If bigger than 1, shape gets bigger (e.g. 2).

2 If between 0 and 1, shape gets smaller (e.g. $\frac{1}{2}$).

3 They give the relative distance of the new and
old points from the centre of enlargement.

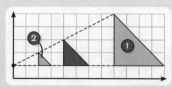

Perimeter and Area

Triangles and Quadrilaterals

PERIMETER — distance around the outside of a shape.

AREA — space taken up by a shape.

Area of rectangle = **length × width**

Squares have equal length and width so area = length^2.

Area of triangle = $\frac{1}{2}$ × **base × vertical height**

h_v is vertical height.

Area of parallelogram = **base × vertical height**

Area of trapezium = $\frac{1}{2}$**(a + b) × vertical height**

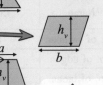

**Split composite shapes into triangles and quadrilaterals.
Work out each area and add together.**

Only include outside edges when adding up perimeters.

5 cm^2

10 cm^2

Total area: 15 cm^2

Circles

diameter (D)

radius (r)

Area = π × (radius)^2
= πr^2

The radius is half the diameter.

Circumference = π × diameter
= πD **OR** = 2 × π × radius
= $2\pi r$

Arcs and Sectors

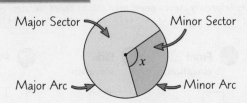

Major Sector

Minor Sector

x

Major Arc

Minor Arc

Area of sector = $\frac{x}{360}$ × **area of full circle**

Length of arc = $\frac{x}{360}$ × **circumference of full circle**

Segments

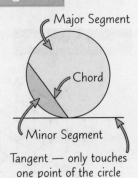

Major Segment

Chord

Minor Segment

Tangent — only touches
one point of the circle

3D Shapes

Eight 3D Shapes

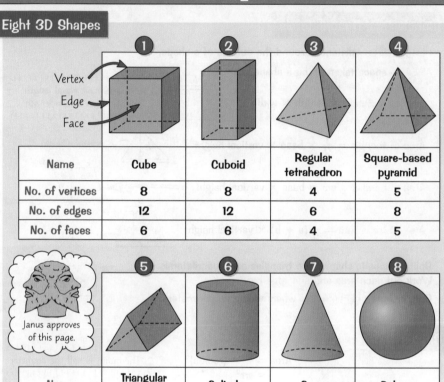

Name	Cube	Cuboid	Regular tetrahedron	Square-based pyramid
No. of vertices	8	8	4	5
No. of edges	12	12	6	8
No. of faces	6	6	4	5

Janus approves of this page.

Name	Triangular prism	Cylinder	Cone	Sphere
No. of vertices	6	0	1	0
No. of edges	9	2	1	0
No. of faces	5	3	2	1

Faces (especially curved ones) may also be called surfaces.

Three Projections

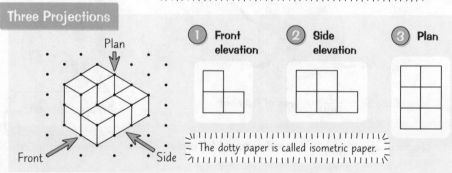

Plan

1 Front elevation

2 Side elevation

3 Plan

Front   Side

The dotty paper is called isometric paper.

Surface Area and Volume

Surface Area Using Nets

SURFACE AREA — total area of all faces.

NET — a 3D shape folded out flat.

Surface area of solid = area of net

EXAMPLE

Sketch the net of the pyramid.

1 square face, 4 triangular faces

Area of square face = 3 × 3 = 9 cm²

Area of triangular face = $\frac{1}{2}$ × 3 × 4 = 6 cm²

Total surface area = 9 + (6 × 4) = 9 + 24 = 33 cm²

Surface Area Formulas

Surface area of sphere = $4\pi r^2$

Surface area of cone = $\pi rl + \pi r^2$

Slant height, not vertical height

Area of the circular base

Surface area of cylinder = $2\pi rh + 2\pi r^2$

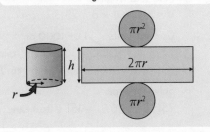

Volumes of Cuboids and Prisms

VOLUME — space inside a 3D shape.

Volume of cuboid = L × W × H

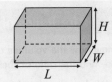

Volume of prism = A × L

A = constant area of cross-section

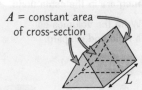

Volume of cylinder = $\pi r^2 h$

Volume

Other Volume Formulas

Volume of sphere
$$= \frac{4}{3}\pi r^3$$

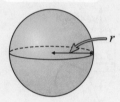

Volume of pyramid
$$= \frac{1}{3} \times \text{base area} \times h_v$$

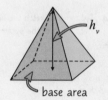

base area

Volume of cone
$$= \frac{1}{3}\pi r^2 h_v$$

Volume of frustum = volume of original cone
− volume of removed cone

A frustum is what's left when the top of a cone is cut off parallel to its base.

$$= \frac{1}{3}\pi R^2 H - \frac{1}{3}\pi r^2 h$$

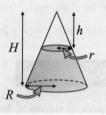

Two Steps for Ratios of Volumes

To show how the volumes of shapes are linked, find the ratio of their volumes:

① Work out each volume separately and make sure they are in the same units.

② Write the volumes as a ratio and simplify.

EXAMPLE

3 cm

2 cm

6 cm

① Volume of sphere $= \frac{4}{3}\pi r^3 = 36\pi$ cm³

Volume of cylinder $= \pi r^2 h = 24\pi$ cm³

② Sphere : cylinder = $36\pi : 24\pi$ = 3 : 2

Rates of Flow

RATE OF FLOW — how fast volume is changing.

The dimensions of shapes are often given in different units to the rate of flow.

EXAMPLE

A cylinder with radius 10 cm and height 8 cm is filled with water at 1 litre per minute. How long does this take to the nearest second?

Find total volume:

$V = \pi \times 10^2 \times 8 = 2513.2...$ cm³

Convert units: 1 L = 1000 cm³

1 L/min × 1000 = 1000 cm³/min

1000 cm³/min ÷ 60 = 16.6... cm³/s

Solve for time:

2513.2... ÷ 16.6... = 151 s (to nearest s)

Angles

Types of Angle

ACUTE angles — less than 90°

RIGHT angles — exactly 90°

OBTUSE angles — between 90° and 180°

REFLEX angles — more than 180°

Angles can be identified using three letters — the middle letter is where the angle is.

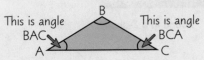

This is angle BAC

This is angle BCA

Three Steps to Measure Angles

1. **Position the protractor** with its base line along one of the angle lines.

2. **Count up in 10° steps** from the start line to the other line of the angle.

3. **Read off the angle** using the correct scale (the one with 0° on the start line).

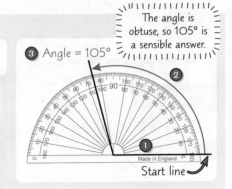

③ Angle = 105°

The angle is obtuse, so 105° is a sensible answer.

Start line

Made in England

Five Angle Rules

1. Angles in a triangle add up to **180°**.

2. Angles on a straight line add up to **180°**.

3. Angles in a quadrilateral add up to **360°**.

4. Angles round a point add up to **360°**.

5. Isosceles triangles have 2 identical sides and 2 identical angles.

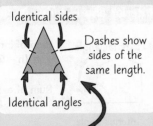

Identical sides

Dashes show sides of the same length.

Identical angles

More Angles

Parallel and Perpendicular Lines

PARALLEL LINES — lines that are always the same distance apart and never meet.

PERPENDICULAR LINES — lines that meet at a right angle.

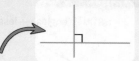

When a line crosses two parallel lines:

- Two bunches of angles are formed.
- There are only two different angles (a and b).
- Vertically opposite angles are equal.

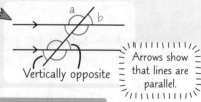

Vertically opposite

Arrows show that lines are parallel.

Alternate Angles

Found in a Z-shape:

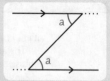

Alternate angles are the same.

Corresponding Angles

Found in an F-shape:

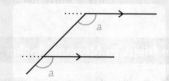

Corresponding angles are the same.

Allied Angles

Found in a C- or U-shape:

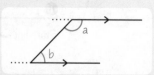

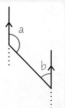

Allied angles add up to 180°.

$$a + b = 180°$$

Interior and Exterior Angles of Polygons

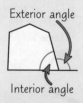

Exterior angle

Interior angle

Sum of interior angles
= (n − 2) × 180°

n = number of sides

Sum of exterior angles
= 360°

Interior angle = 180° − exterior angle

For regular polygons only:

Exterior angle = $\dfrac{360°}{n}$

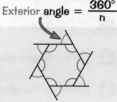

Construction

Triangles — Three Known Sides

① Roughly sketch and label the triangle.

② Accurately draw and label the base line.

③ Set compasses to each side length, then draw an arc at each end.

④ Join up the ends of the base line with the point where the arcs cross. Label points and sides.

EXAMPLE

Construct triangle ABC where AB = 3 cm, BC = 2 cm, AC = 2.5 cm.

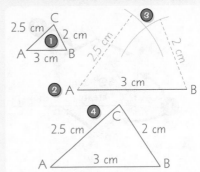

Triangles — Known Sides and Angles

① Roughly sketch and label the triangle.

② Accurately draw and label the base line.

③ Use a protractor to measure any angles and mark out with dots.

④ If you're given two angles, draw lines from the ends of the base line through the dots. Label the intersection.

If you're given two sides, measure towards the dot and label the point.

⑤ Join up the points. Label known sides and angles.

EXAMPLE

Construct triangle XYZ where XY = 2 cm, angle YXZ = 70°, angle XYZ = 40°.

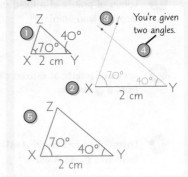

You're given two angles.

Drawing Perpendicular Lines

You'll be given a line and a point.

Keep compass settings the same for both arcs in each step.

Always leave your compass marks visible — don't rub them out.

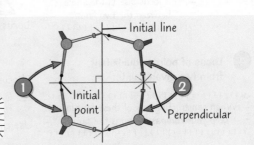

Construction and Loci

Constructing 60° Angles

Keep compass settings the same for 60° angles.

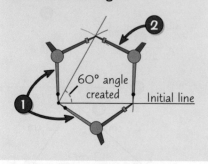

60° angle created

Initial line

Constructing 90° Angles

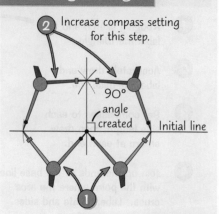

2 Increase compass setting for this step.

90° angle created

Initial line

Four Different Types of Loci

LOCI — lines or regions showing all points that fit a given rule.

1 Locus of points at a fixed distance from a given **point**:

Point

Locus

Low-key entrances weren't really Tracey's style.

2 Locus of points at a fixed distance from a given **line**:

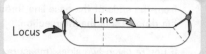

Locus

Line

3 Locus of points equidistant from two given lines:

This locus bisects the angle between the two lines.

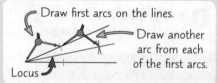

Draw first arcs on the lines.

Draw another arc from each of the first arcs.

Locus

4 Locus of points equidistant from two given points:

When constructing any of these four loci, keep your compass settings the same.

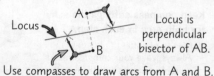

Locus

A

B

Locus is perpendicular bisector of AB.

Use compasses to draw arcs from A and B.

Bearings and Scale Drawings

Bearings

BEARING — a direction given as an angle. Bearings must be given as three figures (e.g. 080° not 80°).

Three steps to find bearings:

1. Put your pencil at the point you're going from.
2. Draw a north line at that point.
3. Measure the angle clockwise from the north line to the line joining the two points.

EXAMPLE

Find the bearing of X from Y.

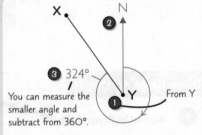

You can measure the smaller angle and subtract from 360°.

324°

So the bearing of X from Y is 324°.

Map Scales

Three types of map scale:

1. 1 cm = 2 km
2. 0 km 2
3. 1 : 200 000

These all mean: "1 cm on the map represents 2 km in real life".

If the scale doesn't have units, use the same units for both sides then convert to sensible units for the context.
E.g. here, 200 000 cm = 2000 m = 2 km

To convert between maps and real life:

Real-life distance ÷ by map scale → Map distance
Real-life distance ← × by map scale Map distance

EXAMPLE

The scale on a map is 1:2000. How far would 2.5 cm on the map be in real life in m?

Multiply by map scale: 2.5 × 2000 = 5000 cm

Convert cm to m: 5000 cm ÷ 100 = 50 m

Scale Drawings

EXAMPLE

0.5 cm represents 1 m

0.5 cm

Table

Sofa

Diagram: 1.5 cm long, 0.5 cm wide
Real life: 3 m long, 1 m wide

Real life: 2 m long, 1 m wide
Diagram: 1 cm long, 0.5 cm wide

Section 6 — Angles and Geometry

Pythagoras' Theorem and Trigonometry

Pythagoras' Theorem

Uses two sides to find third side:

$$a^2 + b^2 = c^2$$

longest side = hypotenuse

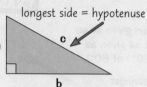

Pythagoras' theorem only works for right-angled triangles.

Three Steps to Use It

1 Square both numbers.

2 To find the longest side, add the two squared numbers.

To find a shorter side, subtract the smaller number from the larger one.

3 Take square root.

EXAMPLE

Find the length of AB to 1 d.p.

9 m   4 m

1 $9^2 = 81$, $4^2 = 16$

2 $AB^2 = AC^2 - BC^2 = 81 - 16$
$= 65$

AB is a shorter side so subtract.

3 $AB = \sqrt{65} = 8.062...$ m
$= 8.1$ m (1 d.p.)

Three Trigonometry Formulas

1 $\text{Sin } x = \dfrac{\text{Opposite}}{\text{Hypotenuse}}$

SOH

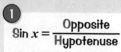

2 $\text{Cos } x = \dfrac{\text{Adjacent}}{\text{Hypotenuse}}$

CAH

3 $\text{Tan } x = \dfrac{\text{Opposite}}{\text{Adjacent}}$

TOA

Opposite (O) — side opposite angle x

Adjacent (A) — side next to angle x

Hypotenuse (H) — the longest side (opposite right angle)

These formulas only work on right-angled triangles.

Remember **SOH CAH TOA** to learn the formulas.

To use a formula triangle:
- Cover up the thing you want.
- Write down whatever's left.

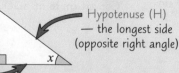

Covering S gives $\sin x = \dfrac{\text{opp}}{\text{hyp}}$

Covering O gives $\text{opp} = \sin x \times \text{hyp}$

Covering H gives $\text{hyp} = \dfrac{\text{opp}}{\sin x}$

Trigonometry

Find a Missing Length

1. Label sides O, A and H.

2. Choose formula.

3. Use a formula triangle to rearrange formula.

4. Put in numbers and work out length.

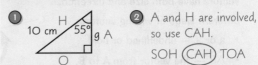

EXAMPLE

Find the length of g to 2 s.f.

1. 10 cm — H — 55° — g A — O

2. A and H are involved, so use CAH.

   SOH (CAH) TOA

3. $\frac{A}{C \times H}$ $A = C \times H$ ← You're finding A.

4. $g = \cos 55° \times 10 = 5.735... = 5.7$ cm (2 s.f.)

Find a Missing Angle

1. Label sides O, A and H.

2. Choose formula.

3. Use a formula triangle to rearrange formula.

4. Put in numbers.

5. Take inverse to find angle.

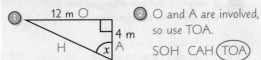

EXAMPLE

Find angle x to 1 d.p.

1. 12 m O — H — 4 m — x A

2. O and A are involved, so use TOA.

   SOH CAH (TOA)

3. $\frac{O}{T \times A}$ $T = \frac{O}{A}$ ← Cover T to find formula.

4. $\tan x = \frac{12}{4} = 3$

5. $x = \tan^{-1}(3) = 71.565...° = 71.6°$ (1 d.p.)

Common Trig Values

Use these common trig values to find exact values in triangles.

$\sin 30° = \frac{1}{2}$ $\sin 60° = \frac{\sqrt{3}}{2}$ $\sin 45° = \frac{1}{\sqrt{2}}$

$\cos 30° = \frac{\sqrt{3}}{2}$ $\cos 60° = \frac{1}{2}$ $\cos 45° = \frac{1}{\sqrt{2}}$

$\tan 30° = \frac{1}{\sqrt{3}}$ $\tan 60° = \sqrt{3}$ $\tan 45° = 1$

$\sin 0° = 0$
$\sin 90° = 1$
$\cos 0° = 1$
$\cos 90° = 0$
$\tan 0° = 0$

Vectors

Vector Notation

Vectors have both size and direction.

Different ways of writing vectors:

- $\underline{a}$ or **a** — underlined or bold

- $\overrightarrow{AB}$ — the vector from A to B.

- $\begin{pmatrix} 5 \\ -3 \end{pmatrix}$ — column vector
  (5 units right, 3 units down)

This vector can be written as:
$\underline{b}$, **b**, $\overrightarrow{CD}$ or $\begin{pmatrix} 4 \\ -1 \end{pmatrix}$.

Multiplying a Vector by a Number

Multiplying a vector by:

+ a positive number changes its size only — its direction stays the same.

− a negative number changes the size and reverses the direction.

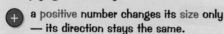
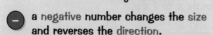
Vectors that are multiples of each other are parallel.

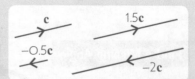

$$a = \begin{pmatrix} -2 \\ 3 \end{pmatrix} \qquad 2a = 2\begin{pmatrix} -2 \\ 3 \end{pmatrix} = \begin{pmatrix} -2 \times 2 \\ 3 \times 2 \end{pmatrix} = \begin{pmatrix} -4 \\ 6 \end{pmatrix}$$

$$-3a = -3\begin{pmatrix} -2 \\ 3 \end{pmatrix} = \begin{pmatrix} -2 \times -3 \\ 3 \times -3 \end{pmatrix} = \begin{pmatrix} 6 \\ -9 \end{pmatrix}$$

Adding and Subtracting Vectors

$\underline{a} + \underline{b}$ means "go along $\underline{a}$ then along $\underline{b}$"

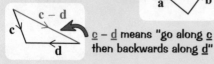
$\underline{c} - \underline{d}$ means "go along $\underline{c}$ then backwards along $\underline{d}$"

To describe a movement between points:

1 Find route made up of known vectors.

2 Add vectors along route. Subtract vectors travelled in reverse direction.

For column vectors: add/subtract top numbers, then add/subtract bottom numbers.

E.g. $\begin{pmatrix} 4 \\ -1 \end{pmatrix} - \begin{pmatrix} 2 \\ 3 \end{pmatrix} = \begin{pmatrix} 4-2 \\ -1-3 \end{pmatrix} = \begin{pmatrix} 2 \\ -4 \end{pmatrix}$

EXAMPLE

Find vector $\overrightarrow{AD}$ in terms of **p** and **q**.

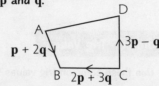

1 $\overrightarrow{AD} = \overrightarrow{AB} + \overrightarrow{BC} + \overrightarrow{CD}$
2 $\quad = (\underline{p} + 2\underline{q}) - (2\underline{p} + 3\underline{q})$
$\quad\quad + (3\underline{p} - \underline{q})$
$\quad = 2\underline{p} - 2\underline{q}$

Watch out for the direction of the arrows — the vector given is actually $\overrightarrow{CB}$ so you need to subtract it to go along $\overrightarrow{BC}$.

Probability Basics

The Probability Scale

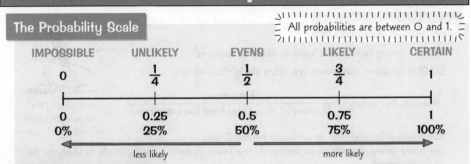

All probabilities are between 0 and 1.

IMPOSSIBLE   UNLIKELY   EVENS   LIKELY   CERTAIN

0               $\frac{1}{4}$ $\frac{1}{2}$ $\frac{3}{4}$ 1

0   0.25   0.5   0.75   1
0%   25%   50%   75%   100%

less likely   more likely

The Probability Formula

$$\text{Probability} = \frac{\text{Number of ways for something to happen}}{\text{Total number of possible outcomes}}$$

You can only use this formula if all the outcomes are equally likely — e.g. for a fair coin, dice or spinner.

EXAMPLE

What is the probability of picking a prime number at random from a bag of counters numbered 1-15?

The prime numbers between 1 and 15 are 2, 3 5, 7, 11 and 13 — 6 in total.

$$\text{Probability} = \frac{\text{number of ways of picking a prime}}{\text{total number of possible outcomes}} = \frac{6}{15} = \frac{2}{5}$$

There are 15 counters so 15 possible outcomes.

Probabilities of Events

If only one possible outcome can happen at a time, the probabilities of all possible outcomes add up to 1. As events either happen or don't:

P(event happens) + P(event doesn't happen) = 1

So:

P(event doesn't happen) = 1 – P(event happens)

EXAMPLE

The probability of getting a 5 on a spinner is 0.65. What is the probability of not getting a 5?

P(not 5) = 1 – P(5)
         = 1 – 0.65 = 0.35

P(event) means "the probability of the event happening".

Sample Space Diagrams

These show all possible outcomes.

Can be a simple list or a two-way table.

You can use them to find probabilities.

×	1	2	3
2	2	4	6
4	4	8	12
6	6	12	18

E.g. All possible outcomes when two fair spinners numbered 1, 2, 3 and 2, 4, 6 are spun and the results multiplied.

There are 9 possible outcomes and 2 of them are 6, so P(6) = $\frac{2}{9}$.

Probability Experiments

Repeating Experiments

FAIR — every outcome is equally likely to happen.

BIASED — some outcomes are more likely than others.

Relative frequency = $\dfrac{\text{Frequency}}{\text{Number of times you tried the experiment}}$

Repeating the experiment hadn't improved Robin's accuracy.

Use relative frequencies to estimate probabilities.
The more times you do an experiment, the more accurate the estimate is likely to be.

EXAMPLE

A spinner labelled A to D is spun 100 times. It lands on C 48 times.
Find the relative frequency of spinning a C and say whether you think this spinner is biased.

Relative frequency of C = $\dfrac{48}{100}$ = 0.48

If the spinner was fair, you'd expect the relative frequency of C to be 1 ÷ 4 = 0.25.
0.48 is much larger than 0.25, so the spinner is probably biased.

Frequency Trees

Used to record results when experiments have more than one step. For example:

Choir?

Form Yes (14) ← 14 pupils from 11A are in the choir

11A (27)

No (13) ← Relative frequency of pupils in 11A and not in choir = $\dfrac{13}{50}$ = 0.26

Total number of pupils → (50)

11B

Yes (8)

(23)

No (15) ← 13 + 15 = 28 pupils aren't in the choir

23 pupils in Form 11B →

Expected Frequency

EXPECTED FREQUENCY — how many times you'd expect something to happen in a certain number of trials.

Expected frequency
= probability × number of trials

Use the relative frequency from previous experiments if you don't know the probability.

EXAMPLE

A fair 6-sided dice is rolled 360 times. How many times would you expect it to land on 4?

P(4) = $\dfrac{1}{6}$

Expected frequency of 4 = $\dfrac{1}{6}$ × 360

= 60

The AND/OR Rule and Tree Diagrams

The AND Rule

INDEPENDENT EVENTS — where one event happening doesn't affect the probability of another event happening.

For independent events A and B:

$$P(A \text{ and } B) = P(A) \times P(B)$$

This rule only works for independent events.

EXAMPLE

A fair dice is rolled and a fair coin is tossed. What is the probability of rolling a 2 and getting heads?

$P(2) = \frac{1}{6}$ and $P(\text{heads}) = \frac{1}{2}$

Rolling a dice and tossing a coin are independent, so:

$P(2 \text{ and heads}) = \frac{1}{6} \times \frac{1}{2} = \frac{1}{12}$

The OR Rule

Use the OR rule when events can't happen at the same time.

For events A and B:

$$P(A \text{ or } B) = P(A) + P(B)$$

EXAMPLE

A bag contains 12 balls numbered 1–12. What is the probability of selecting either an even number or a 5?

$P(\text{even}) = \frac{6}{12}$ and $P(5) = \frac{1}{12}$

So $P(\text{even or } 5) = \frac{6}{12} + \frac{1}{12} = \frac{7}{12}$

Tree Diagrams

Used to work out probabilities for combinations of events — e.g. for a bag containing 3 red and 2 blue counters that are selected at random and without replacement:

Probabilities on each set of branches that meet at a point add up to 1.

Multiply along the branches to get the end probabilities.

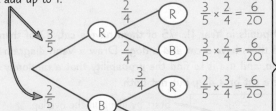

The second selection is affected by the results of the first — so the probabilities are different.

If the counters were replaced, the probabilities on each set of branches would be the same.

The end probabilities add up to 1:
$\frac{6}{20} + \frac{6}{20} + \frac{6}{20} + \frac{2}{20} = \frac{20}{20} = 1$

Pick the right end probability to answer questions:

E.g. $P(B, B) = \frac{2}{20} = \frac{1}{10}$

Sets and Venn Diagrams

Set Notation

SET — a collection of elements
(e.g. numbers), written in curly brackets {}.

Sets can be written in different ways:
- **list of elements** — e.g. A = {1, 4, 9, 16}
- **description** — e.g. A = {square numbers less than 20}
- **formal notation** — e.g. A = {x : x is a square number less than 20}

$\in$	'is a member of'. So $x \in A$ means x is a member of A.
ξ	the universal set (the group of things elements are selected from).
n(A)	the number of elements in set **A**.

Sets and Venn Diagrams

VENN DIAGRAM — a diagram where sets are represented by overlapping circles.
The rectangle represents the universal set.

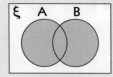 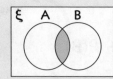 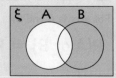

A ∪ B — the union of
sets A and B (everything
inside the circles)

A ∩ B — the intersection
of sets A and B (everything
in the overlap)

A′ — the complement of
set A (everything outside
the circle for A)

Probabilities from Venn Diagrams

Venn diagrams can show either the number of elements or the elements themselves.

EXAMPLE

There are 150 pupils in Year 11. 75 of them have a cat, 92 of them have a
dog and 22 of them have a cat and a dog. Draw a Venn diagram to show
this information, and use it to find the probability that a randomly selected
pupil will have a cat or a dog, but not both.

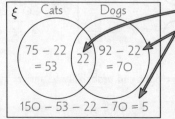

Start by filling in the overlap.

Then subtract to find the missing numbers.

Add up the numbers in the circles that aren't
in the overlap and divide by the total:
P(cat or dog but not both)

$$= \frac{53 + 70}{150} = \frac{123}{150} = \frac{41}{50}$$

Sampling and Data Collection

Definitions of Sampling Terms

POPULATION	The whole group you want to find out about.
SAMPLE	A smaller group taken from the population.
RANDOM SAMPLE	A sample in which every member of the population has an equal chance of being included.
REPRESENTATIVE	Fairly represents the whole population.
BIASED	Doesn't fairly represent the whole population.
QUALITATIVE DATA	Data described by words (not numbers).
QUANTITATIVE DATA	Data described by numbers.
DISCRETE DATA	Data that can only take exact values.
CONTINUOUS DATA	Data that can take any value in a range.

Choosing a Simple Random Sample

1. Give each member of the population a number.

2. Make a list of random numbers.

3. Pick the members of the population with those numbers.

Random numbers can be chosen using a computer/calculator, or from a bag.

Spotting Bias

Two things to think about:

1. When, where and how the sample is taken.

2. How big the sample is.

- If any groups have been excluded, it won't be random.
- If it isn't big enough, it won't be representative.
- Bigger samples should be more reliable.

Questionnaires

Questions should be:

- Clear and easy to understand
  e.g. specifies a time period
- Easy to answer
- Fair (not leading or biased)

How long do you spend exercising each week?

☐ < 1 hour
☐ ≥ 1 and < 3 hours
☐ ≥ 3 and < 5 hours
☐ ≥ 5 hours

Response boxes should be:

- Cover all possible options
  e.g. 'more than' and 'less than' options
- Not overlap
  e.g. 1 hour can only go in one box
- Not be interpreted in different ways

Simple Charts and Graphs

Pictograms

PICTOGRAM — uses symbols to show frequency.

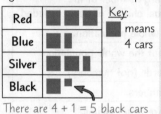

E.g. number of cars in a car park

Red				Key:
Blue				■ means
Silver				4 cars
Black				

There are 4 + 1 = 5 black cars

Bar Charts

BAR CHART — height of bar shows frequency.
Use dual bar charts to compare data sets.

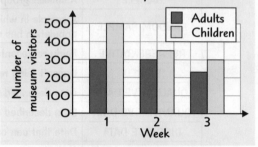

Two-Way Tables

TWO-WAY TABLE — shows how many there are in each category.

	Likes honey	Doesn't like honey	Total
Year 10	85	73	158
Year 11	96	82	178
Total	181	155	336

To fill in a two-way table, add/subtract using the information you're given to find missing values.

Stem and Leaf Diagrams

STEM AND LEAF DIAGRAM — puts data in order and shows the spread.
Use them to find averages and range.

Range = 3.3 m − 0.5 m = 2.8 m
Mode = 2.7 m   Median = 2.1 m

Time Series

TIME SERIES — a line graph showing the same thing measured at different times.
A time series shows if there is seasonality (a basic repeating pattern).

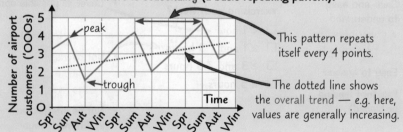

This pattern repeats itself every 4 points.

The dotted line shows the overall trend — e.g. here, values are generally increasing.

Pie Charts

Pie Charts and Proportion

Total of all data = 360°

Work out missing angles and fractions of the total using the information given.

This pie chart shows how some pupils travel to school.

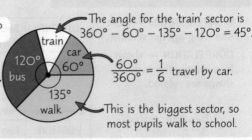

The angle for the 'train' sector is 360° − 60° − 135° − 120° = 45°.

$\frac{60°}{360°} = \frac{1}{6}$ travel by car.

This is the biggest sector, so most pupils walk to school.

Four Steps to Draw Pie Charts

1. Add up the numbers to find the total.

2. Divide 360° by the total to find the multiplier.

3. Multiply each number by the multiplier to find the angle.

4. Draw the pie chart accurately using a protractor.

EXAMPLE

1. Total = 15 + 8 + 17 = 40
2. Multiplier = 360° ÷ 40 = 9°

Club	Drama	Art	Band
Number	15	8	17
Angle	135°	72°	153°

3. E.g. 15 × 9° = 135°

4.

Check that the angles add up to 360°:
135° + 72° + 153° = 360°

Two Steps to Find How Many in a Category

1. Divide 360° by the total to find the angle for one item.

2. Divide the angle for a category by the angle for one item.

My favourite types of pie (I've already eaten the Key lime slice).

EXAMPLE

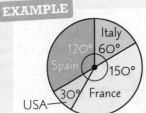

120 pupils were asked where they went on holiday last summer. The results are shown in the pie chart. How many pupils went to Italy?

1. 360° ÷ 120 = 3° per pupil
2. 60° ÷ 3° = 20 pupils went to Italy

Scatter Graphs

Scatter Graphs and Correlation

SCATTER GRAPH — plots one thing against another.

CORRELATION — shows how closely the two things are related.

Even if two things are correlated, it doesn't mean that one causes the other.

STRONG correlation	Two things are closely related. Points make a fairly straight line.
WEAK correlation	Two things are loosely related. Points don't line up quite as neatly.
NO correlation	Two things are unrelated. Points are scattered randomly.
POSITIVE correlation	Two things increase or decrease together. Points slope uphill from left to right.
NEGATIVE correlation	One thing increases as the other decreases. Points slope downhill from left to right.

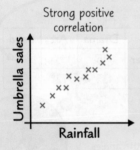

Strong positive correlation

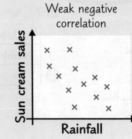

Weak negative correlation

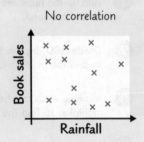

No correlation

Lines of Best Fit

LINE OF BEST FIT — goes through or near most points. Shows correlation and can be used to make predictions.

OUTLIER — a point that doesn't fit the general pattern. Ignore it when drawing the line of best fit.

INTERPOLATION — predicting within the range of data. Usually reliable. Here, you'd expect a 2-year-old car to be worth about £5000.

EXTRAPOLATION — predicting outside the range of data. Can be unreliable. Here, a 5-year-old car might be worth about £600, but this could be unreliable.

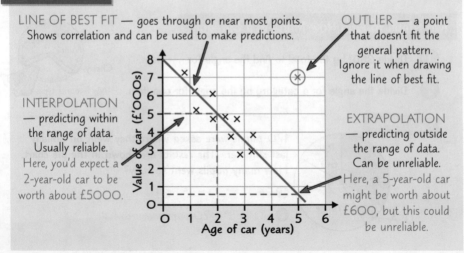

Mean, Median, Mode and Range

Mean, Median, Mode and Range

MEAN	Total of values ÷ number of values
MEDIAN	Middle value (when values are in size order)
MODE	Most common value
RANGE	Difference between highest and lowest values

Arrange the data in order of size to find the median. It helps when finding the mode and range too.

To find the position of the median, use the formula: **(n + 1) ÷ 2**

(where n is the number of items)

EXAMPLE

The data below shows the ages of people in a judo club.
Find the mean, median, mode and range for the data.

24   28   17   34   36   24   19   26

The mean, median and mode are all averages.

Mean = $\dfrac{24+28+17+34+36+24+19+26}{8} = \dfrac{208}{8}$ = 26 years

In order: 17   19   24   ⟨24   26⟩   28   34   36
Position of median = (8 + 1) ÷ 2 = 4.5th value.
So median is halfway between 24 and 26, which is 25 years.
Mode = 24 years   Range = 36 − 17 = 19 years

If a data set has an outlier, it can have a big effect on the mean and range, making them misleading.

If a 62-year-old joined the judo club, this person would be an outlier. It would make the mean 30 and the range 45, which do not represent the rest of the data well.

Comparing Data Sets

Look at the averages and range for each data set, identify which is higher or lower and say what they mean in the context of the data.

EXAMPLE

Some statistics for the members of a karate club are shown on the right. Compare the distribution of the ages of the karate club and the judo club.

Mean: 22 years
Median: 23 years
Range: 10 years

The mean and median values for the karate club are lower than the values for the judo club, so the members of the karate club are generally younger.

The range for the karate club is lower than the range for the judo club, so there is less variation in ages for the karate club — members' ages are more consistent.

Finding Averages

Finding Averages from Frequency Tables

FREQUENCY TABLE — shows how many things there are in each category.

This frequency table shows how many different school clubs some students attend.

MODE — category with the highest frequency.
Here it's 2.

MEDIAN — category containing the middle value.
The median is the $(25 + 1) ÷ 2 = $ 13th value, which is in the category '2'.

RANGE — difference between the highest and lowest categories.
Range = 3 − 0 = 3

Number of clubs (x)	Frequency (f)	Number of clubs × Frequency ($f × x$)
0	4	0
1	7	7
2	9	18
3	5	15
Total	25	40

$$\text{MEAN} = \frac{\text{total (category} × \text{frequency)}}{\text{total frequency}} = \frac{40}{25} = 1.6$$

Grouped Frequency Tables

Data is grouped into classes, with no gaps between classes for continuous data.

Inequality symbols are used to cover all possible values.

Height (h cm)	Frequency (f)	Mid-interval value (x)	$f × x$
0 < h ≤ 20	12	10	120
20 < h ≤ 30	28	25	700
30 < h ≤ 40	10	35	350
Total	50	—	1170

Find the mid-interval value by adding up the end values and dividing by 2.
E.g. $(0 + 20) ÷ 2 = 10$.

Mid-interval popcorn

MODAL CLASS — class with highest frequency.
Here it's 20 < h ≤ 30.

CLASS CONTAINING THE MEDIAN — contains the middle piece of data.
The median is the $(50 + 1) ÷ 2 = $ 25.5th value. Both the 25th and 26th data values are in the 20 < h ≤ 30 class, so the class containing the median is 20 < h ≤ 30.

RANGE — difference between the highest and lowest class boundaries.
Estimated range = 40 − 0 = 40 cm

MEAN — multiply the mid-interval value (x) by the frequency (f). Divide the total of f × x by the total frequency.
Estimated mean = $\frac{1170}{50} = 23.4$ cm

You don't know the actual values for grouped data so can only estimate the mean and range.

MQFNO41_MXFNO41